Glencoe Mathematics

Pre-Algebra

Chapter 12
Resource Masters

Mc Graw Hill **Glencoe**

New York, New York   Columbus, Ohio   Chicago, Illinois   Peoria, Illinois   Woodland Hills, California

Consumable Workbooks Many of the worksheets contained in the Chapter Resource Masters are available as consumable workbooks in both English and Spanish.

	ISBN10	ISBN13
Study Guide and Intervention Workbook	0-07-877224-1	978-0-07-877224-6
Skills Practice Workbook	0-07-877216-8	978-0-07-877216-0
Practice Workbook	0-07-877218-4	978-0-07-877218-4
Word Problem Practice Workbook	0-07-877220-6	978-0-07-877220-7

Spanish Versions

Study Guide and Intervention Workbook	0-07-877224-1	978-0-07-877224-6
Skills Practice Workbook	0-07-877217-6	978-0-07-877217-7
Practice Workbook	0-07-877219-2	978-0-07-877219-1
Word Problem Practice Workbook	0-07-877221-4	978-0-07-877221-4

Answers for Workbooks The answers for Chapter 12 of these workbooks can be found in the back of this Chapter Resource Masters booklet.

StudentWorks Plus™ This CD-ROM includes the entire Student Edition test along with the English workbooks listed above.

TeacherWorks Plus™ All of the materials found in this booklet are included for viewing, printing, and editing in this CD-ROM.

Spanish Assessment Masters (ISBN10: 0-07-877222-2, ISBN13: 978-0-07-877222-1) These masters contain a Spanish version of Chapter 12 Test Form 2A and Form 2C.

 **Glencoe**

The McGraw·Hill Companies

Send all inquiries to:
Glencoe/McGraw-Hill
8787 Orion Place
Columbus, OH 43240

ISBN13: 978-0-07-873942-2
ISBN10: 0-07-873942-X

Printed in the United States of America

2 3 4 5 6 7 8 9 10 024 13 12 11 10 09 08 07

Contents

Teacher's Guide to Using the Chapter 12 Resource Masters

The *Chapter 12 Resource Masters* includes the core materials needed for Chapter 12. These materials include worksheets, extensions, and assessment options. The answers for these pages appear at the back of this booklet.

All of the materials found in this booklet are included for viewing and printing in the *TeacherWorks Plus*™ CD-ROM.

Chapter Resources

Student-Built Glossary (pages 1–2) These masters are a student study tool that presents up to twenty of the key vocabulary terms from the chapter. Students are to record definitions and/or examples for each term. You may suggest that students highlight or star the terms with which they are not familiar. Give this to students before beginning Lesson 12-1. Encourage them to add these pages to their mathematics study notebooks. Remind them to complete the appropriate words as they study each lesson.

Anticipation Guide (pages 3–4) This master, presented in both English and Spanish, is a survey used before beginning the chapter to pinpoint what students may or may not know about the concepts in the chapter. Students will revisit this survey after they complete the chapter to see if their perceptions have changed.

Lesson Resources

Lesson Reading Guide Get Ready for the Lesson extends the discussion from the beginning of the Student Edition lesson. Read the Lesson asks students to interpret the context of and relationships among terms in the lesson. Finally, Remember What You Learned asks students to summarize what they have learned using various representation techniques. Use as a study tool for note taking or as an informal reading assignment. It is also a helpful tool for ELL (English Language Learners).

Study Guide and Intervention This master provides vocabulary, key concepts, additional worked-out examples and Check Your Progress exercises to use as a reteaching activity. It can also be used in conjunction with the Student Edition as an instructional tool for students who have been absent.

Skills Practice This master focuses more on the computational nature of the lesson. Use as an additional practice option or as homework for second-day teaching of the lesson.

Practice This master closely follows the types of problems found in the Exercises section of the Student Edition and includes word problems. Use as an additional practice option or as homework for second-day teaching of the lesson.

Word Problem Practice This master includes additional practice in solving word problems that apply the concepts of the lesson. Use as an additional practice or as homework for second-day teaching of the lesson.

Enrichment These activities may extend the concepts of the lesson, offer an historical or multicultural look at the concepts, or widen students' perspectives on the mathematics they are learning. They are written for use with all levels of students.

Graphing Calculator, Scientific Calculator, or Spreadsheet Activities

These activities present ways in which technology can be used with the concepts in some lessons of this chapter. Use as an alternative approach to some concepts or as an integral part of your lesson presentation.

Assessment Options

The assessment masters in the *Chapter 12 Resource Masters* offer a wide range of assessment tools for formative (monitoring) assessment and summative (final) assessment.

Student Recording Sheet This master corresponds with the standardized test practice at the end of the chapter.

Pre-AP Rubric This master provides information for teachers and students on how to assess performance on open-ended questions.

Quizzes Four free-response quizzes offer assessment at appropriate intervals in the chapter.

Mid-Chapter Test This 1-page test provides an option to assess the first half of the chapter. It parallels the timing of the Mid-Chapter Quiz in the Student Edition and includes both multiple-choice and free-response questions.

Vocabulary Test This test is suitable for all students. It includes a list of vocabulary words and 10 questions to assess students' knowledge of those words. This can also be used in conjunction with one of the leveled chapter tests.

Leveled Chapter Tests

- *Form 1* contains multiple-choice questions and is intended for use with below grade level students.
- *Forms 2A and 2B* contain multiple-choice questions aimed at on grade level students. These tests are similar in format to offer comparable testing situations.
- *Forms 2C and 2D* contain free-response questions aimed at on grade level students. These tests are similar in format to offer comparable testing situations.
- *Form 3* is a free-response test for use with above grade level students.

All of the above tests include a free-response Bonus question.

Extended-Response Test Performance assessment tasks are suitable for all students. Sample answers and a scoring rubric are included for evaluation.

Standardized Test Practice These three pages are cumulative in nature. It includes three parts: multiple-choice questions with bubble-in answer format, griddable questions with answer grids, and short-answer free-response questions.

Answers

- The answers for the Anticipation Guide and Lesson Resources are provided as reduced pages with answers appearing in red.
- Full-size answer keys are provided for the assessment masters.

12 Student-Built Glossary

This is an alphabetical list of key vocabulary terms you will learn in Chapter 12.
As you study this chapter, complete each term's definition or description.
Remember to add the page number where you found the term. Add these pages to
your Pre-Algebra Study Notebook to review vocabulary at the end of the chapter.

Vocabulary Term	Found on Page	Definition/Description/Example
back-to-back stem-and-leaf plot		
box-and-whisker plot		
combination		
composite events		
dependent events		
experimental probability		
Fundamental Counting Principle		
histogram		
independent events		
interquartile range IN-tuhr-KWAWR-tyl		
measures of variation		

12 Student-Built Glossary (continued)

Vocabulary Term	Found on Page	Definition/Description/Example
mutually exclusive events		
odds		
outcomes		
outlier		
permutation PUHR-myoo-TAY-shuhn		
probability		
quartiles		
range		
sample space		
simple event		
stem-and-leaf plot		
theoretical probability		
tree diagram		
upper and lower quartiles		

12 Anticipation Guide

Equations

Step 1   *Before you begin Chapter 12*

- Read each statement.

- Decide whether you Agree (A) or Disagree (D) with the statement.

- Write A or D in the first column OR if you are not sure whether you agree or disagree, write NS (Not Sure).

STEP 1 A, D, or NS	Statement	Step 2 A or D
	1. A stem-and-leave plot organizes data in numerical order.	
	2. It is always better to display data in a stem-and-leave plot than a table.	
	3. The range of a set of data is the sum of the data divided by the number of items in the data set.	
	4. A box-and-whisker plot usually contains a *box* with *whiskers* extending from each side.	
	5. In a box-and-whisker plot, the median always divides the box in half.	
	6. *Histogram* is another name for a bar graph.	
	7. It does not matter which type of display is chosen for a set of data because all types show the same information.	
	8. Two bar graphs for the same set of data can give different impressions about that data by using a different scale for each graph.	
	9. Probability tells how likely an event is to occur.	
	10. If the probability of an event is 30%, most likely that event will occur.	
	11. A tree diagram can be used to count all possible outcomes in a problem.	
	12. All probabilities range from 0 to 1.	

Step 2   *After you complete Chapter 12*

- Reread each statement and complete the last column by entering an A (Agree) or a D (Disagree).

- Did any of your opinions about the statements change from the first column?

- For those statements that you mark with a D, use a separate sheet of paper to explain why you disagree. Use examples, if possible.

12 Ejercicios preparatorios

Más estadíticas y probabilidad

- Lee cada enunciado.
- Decide si estás de acuerdo (A) o en desacuerdo (D) con el enunciado.
- Escribe A o D en la primera columna O si no estás seguro(a) de la respuesta, escribe NS (No estoy seguro(a)).

PASO 1 A, D o NS	Enunciado	PASO 2 A o D
	1. Un diagrama de tallo y hojas organiza información en orden numérico.	
	2. Siempre es mejor representar información en un diagrama de tallos y hojas que en una tabla.	
	3. El rango de un conjunto de datos es la suma de los datos dividida entre el número de datos en el conjunto.	
	4. Un diagrama de caja y patillas contiene, por lo general, una *caja* con *patillas* que se extienden desde cada lado.	
	5. En un diagrama de caja y patillas, la media siempre divide la caja por la mitad.	
	6. *Histograma* es otro nombre para gráfica de barras.	
	7. El tipo de representación que se escoge para un conjunto de datos no es importante porque todos ellos muestran la misma información.	
	8. Dos gráficas de barras para el mismo conjunto de datos pueden dar impresiones diferentes acerca de los datos cuando se usa una escala diferente para cada gráfica.	
	9. La probabilidad establece el porcentaje de posibilidad de que ocurra un evento.	
	10. Si la probabilidad de un evento es de 30%, muy posiblemente el evento ocurrirá.	
	11. Puede usarse un diagrama de árbol para contar todos los posibles resultados en un problema.	
	12. Todas las probabilidades están en un rango de 0 a 1.	

Paso 2   *Después de completar el Capítulo 12*

- Vuelve a leer cada enunciado y completa la última columna con una A o una D.
- ¿Cambió cualquiera de tus opiniones sobre los enunciados de la primera columna?
- En una hoja de papel aparte, escribe un ejemplo de por qué estás en desacuerdo con los enunciados que marcaste con una D.

12-1 Lesson Reading Guide

Stem-and-Leaf Plots

Get Ready for the Lesson

Read the introduction to Lesson 12-1 in your textbook. Write your answers below.

a. Is there an equal number of electors in each group? Explain.

b. Name an advantage of displaying the data in groups.

Read the Lesson

Write a definition and give an example of each new vocabulary word or phrase.

Vocabulary	Definition	Example
1. stem-and-leaf plot		
2. stems		
3. leaves		
4. back-to-back stem-and-leaf plot		

Remember What You Learned

5. How will you remember which numbers of a stem-and-leaf plot represent the greater place value? Use the data to draw a back-to-back stem-and-leaf plot like actual leaves on stems. Read the data from the tree trunk and move outward.

Ages of Persons							
Apartment Building A			Apartment Building B				
33	16	19	39	21	20	1	
26	23	11	10	21	36	37	
34	24	37	32	22	11	2	
17	29		10	1	32	38	
			12	36	39		

12-1 Study Guide and Intervention

Stem-and-Leaf Plots

Stem-and-Leaf Plot	**Words**	One way to organize and display data is to use a **stem-and-leaf plot**. In a stem and leaf plot, numerical data are listed in ascending or descending order.

Model

Stem	Leaf
2	0 1 1 2 3 5 5 6
3	1 2 2 3 7 9
4	0 3 4 8 8

$3 \mid 7 = 37$

The greatest place value of the data is used for the **stems**.

The next greatest place value forms the **leaves**.

Example ZOOS Display the data shown at the right in a stem-and-leaf plot.

Step 1 The least and the greatest numbers are 55 and 95. The greatest place value digit in each number is in the tens. Draw a vertical line and write the stems from 5 to 9 to the left of the line.

Stem	Leaf
5	8 5
6	4
7	5
8	5 0 0
9	5 0 2

Step 2 Write the leaves to the right of the line, with the corresponding stem. For example, for 85, write 5 to the right of 8.

Step 3 Rearrange the leaves so they are ordered from least to greatest. Then include a key or an explanation.

Stem	Leaf
5	5 8
6	4
7	5
8	0 0 5
9	0 2 5

$8 \mid 5 = 85$ acres

Size of U. S. Zoos	
Zoo	**Size (acres)**
Audubon (New Orleans)	58
Cincinnati	85
Dallas	95
Denver	80
Houston	55
Los Angeles	80
Oregon	64
St. Louis	90
San Francisco	75
Woodland Park (Seattle)	92

Exercises

Display each set of data in a stem-and-leaf plot.

1. {27, 35, 39, 27, 24, 33, 18, 19}

2. {94, 83, 88, 77, 95, 99, 88, 87}

ROLLER COASTERS For Exercises 3 and 4, use the stem-and-leaf plot shown.

3. What is the speed of the fastest roller coaster? The slowest?

4. What is the median speed?

The Fastest Roller Coasters

Stem	Leaf
8	3 5
9	2 5
10	0

$8 \mid 3 = 83$ mph

12-1 Skills Practice

Stem-and-Leaf Plots

Display each set of data in a stem-and-leaf plot.

1. {7, 2, 3, 11, 20, 21, 17, 15, 15, 14}

2. {8, 2, 14, 27, 7, 2, 16, 13, 29, 16}

3.

Amount of Fresh Fruit Consumed per Person in the United States, 2002	
Fruit	**Pounds Consumed per Person**
Apples	16
Bananas	27
Cantaloupes	11
Grapefruit	5
Grapes	9
Oranges	11
Peaches and nectarines	5
Pears	3
Pineapples	4
Plums and prunes	1
Strawberries	5
Watermelons	14

Source: U.S. Census Bureau

4.

Winning Scores in College Football Bowl Games, 2004	
Game and Winning School	**Points Scored**
Alamo Bowl, Nebraska	17
Fiesta Bowl, Ohio St.	35
Gator Bowl, Maryland	41
Holiday Bowl, Washington St.	28
Liberty Bowl, Utah	17
New Orleans Bowl, Memphis	27
Orange Bowl, Miami	16
Outback Bowl, Iowa	37
Peach Bowl, Clemson	27
Rose Bowl, Oklahoma	34
Sugar Bowl, Louisiana St.	21
Tangerine Bowl, N. Carolina St.	56

Source: footballabout.com

HUMIDITY   For Exercises 5–7, use the information in the back-to-back stem-and-leaf plot.   **Source:** The New York Public Library Desk Reference

5. What is the highest morning relative humidity?

6. What is the lowest afternoon relative humidity?

7. Does relative humidity tend to be higher in the morning or afternoon?

U.S. Average Relative Humidity (percent)

Morning		Afternoon
	5	1 2 3 4 7 9
	6	
8 8 4	7	
9 4 0	8	

8 | 7 = 78%   5 | 3 = 53%

12-1 Practice

Stem-and-Leaf Plots

Display each set of data in a stem-and-leaf plot.

1. {68, 63, 70, 59,
78, 64, 68, 73,
61, 66, 70}

2. {27, 32, 42, 31, 36,
37, 47, 23, 39,
31, 41, 38, 30,
34, 29, 42, 37}

3.

Major League Baseball Leading Pitchers, 2005	
Player and Team	**Wins**
C. Capuano	18
C. Carpenter	21
B. Colon	21
J. Garland	18
R. Johnson	17
C. Lee	18
J. Lieber	17
R. Oswalt	20
A. Pettitte	17
D. Willis	22

Source: sports.espn.go.com

4.

Average Prices Received by U.S. Farmers, 2004	
Commodity	**Price (dollars per 100 pounds)**
Beef Cattle	86
Hogs	49
Lambs	101
Milk	16
Veal Calves	119

Source: *U. S Department of Agriculture*

RECREATION For Exercises 5–7, use the information in the back-to-back stem-and-leaf plot shown at the right.

5. The category with the lowest total expenditure in 1992 was motion pictures. What was its total?

6. What is the median total recreational spending for 1992? For 2002?

7. Compare the total spending on recreation in 1992 with that in 2002.

Total U.S. Spending on Personal Recreation (by Category)

1992		2002
7 5 5	0	9
8 7 2 0	1	0 2 8
7 2	2	2
4 0	3	4 5 7
	4	4
	5	6
1	6	0
	7	
	8	4
	9	

7 | 2 = $27 billion   3 | 5 = $35 billion

12-1 **Word Problem Practice**
Stem-and-Leaf Plots

1. CUSTOMER SERVICE A restaurant owner recorded the average time in minutes customers waited to be seated each night. His data are shown in the table below. To organize the data into a stem-and-leaf plot, how many stems would you need?

Week 1	15	8	10	5	20	35	45
Week 2	9	3	7	8	25	38	43

2. PHONE Allison's mother makes a stem-and-leaf plot to track the time in minutes that Allison spends talking on the phone each night. In which interval are most of the Allison's calls?

Stem	Leaf
1	0 5
2	3 4 5 8 9
3	0 5 8
4	1 3 5

1|5 =15 minutes

3. ELECTRIC BILLS Jenny's family is selling their house. Jenny's mother wants to put together a table of monthly electricity costs. Below is a list of their electric bills for the past twelve months. Organize the data in a stem-and-leaf plot. In which interval are most of the electric bills?

$95, $99, $85, $79, $82, $88,

$98, $95, $94, $87, $89, $90

4. TEST SCORES The scores from the most recent test in Mr. James' biology class are shown in the stem-and-leaf plot below. Find the highest and lowest scores, and then write a statement that describes the data.

Stem	Leaf
5	4 5
6	3 7 8
7	0 1 5 5 8 9
8	0 2 3 7 9
9	0 3 5 8 8

5|4 =54%

SPORTS For Exercises 5–7, use the following information.

Tamara and LaDawn have recorded their times in seconds in the 100-meter dash from the past six track meets in the table below.

LaDawn	16.5	16.6	17.0	16.8	17.2	17.1
Tamara	16.7	16.4	16.1	17.0	16.5	16.8

5. Organize the times in a back-to-back stem-and-leaf plot.

6. What are the median times for LaDawn and for Tamara?

7. If you were the coach, who would you choose to represent the team at the next competition? Explain.

Lesson 12-1

12-1 Enrichment

U.S. Presidents

The political parties in our country have changed over time. At the time of our nation's founding, the Federalist and Democratic-Republican parties were the nationally prominent parties. In recent years, all U.S. Presidents have been from either the Republican or Democratic Party.

1. Make a table to display the data for the number of U.S. Presidents from each political party.

Republican	Democrat	Federalist
Abraham Lincoln	Andrew Jackson	George Washington
Ulysses S. Grant	Martin Van Buren	John Adams
Rutherford B. Hayes	James K. Polk	
James A. Garfield	Franklin Pierce	**Democratic-Republican**
Chester A. Arthur	James Buchanan	Thomas Jefferson
Benjamin Harrison	Grover Cleveland	James Madison
William McKinley	Woodrow Wilson	James Monroe
Theodore Roosevelt	Franklin D. Roosevelt	John Quincy Adams
William Howard Taft	Harry S Truman	
Warren G. Harding	John F. Kennedy	**Whig**
Calvin Coolidge	Lyndon B. Johnson	William Henry Harrison
Herbert Hoover	Jimmy Carter	John Tyler
Dwight D. Eisenhower	Bill Clinton	Zachary Taylor
Richard Nixon		Millard Fillmore
Gerald Ford		
Ronald Reagan		**Union**
George Bush		Andrew Johnson
George W. Bush		

2. Display the data from the table in a stem-and-leaf plot.

3. What is the difference in the number of presidents from the party with the most presidents and the party with the fewest presidents?

4. What is another type of information about U.S. Presidents that could be displayed using a stem-and-leaf plot?

12-1 Graphing Calculator Activity

Stem-and-Leaf Plots

The graphing calculator can be used to help make stem-and-leaf plots.

Example   **Make a stem-and-leaf plot from the ages of the U.S. Presidents at their deaths.**

67 90 83 85 73 80 78 79 68 71 53 65 74 64 77 56 66 63 70
49 56 71 67 71 58 60 72 67 57 60 90 63 88 78 46 64 81 93

Source: *The World Almanac*

Before entering the data into the lists, clear the lists of previous data. Enter the data in **L1**. Next, use the sort feature of the calculator to place the data in ascending order. Then, use the sorted list to create a stem-and-leaf plot.

Keystrokes: [STAT] 4 [2nd] **[L1]** [STAT] [ENTER] 67 [ENTER] 90 [ENTER] 83
[ENTER] 85 [ENTER] ... 46 [ENTER] 64 [ENTER] 81 [ENTER] [STAT] 2 [2nd] **[L1]** [ )]
[ENTER] [STAT] [ENTER] [▼].

Stem	Leaf
4	6 9
5	3 6 6 7 8
6	0 0 3 3 4 4 5 6 7 7 7 8
7	0 1 1 1 2 3 4 7 8 8 9
8	0 1 3 5 8
9	0 0 3

$4 \mid 6 = 46$

Exercises

Create a stem-and-leaf plot for each set of data.

1. 83 65 89 88 72 70 66 65 71 64 81 83 84 83
82 64 72 75 88 67 72 81 70 67 89 72 81 70

2. 13.8 14.8 14.3 12.7 12.2 13.9 11.8 10.2 15.7
12.1 13.3 13.6 11.4 12.2 12.7 12.8 14.3 14.4

3. Press [STAT] [ENTER] to verify that the data from Exercise 2 is in **L1**. Then press [MATH] [▶]
2 [2nd] **[L1]** [,] 0 [ )] [STO▶] [2nd] **[L2]** [ENTER] 10 [MATH] [▶] 3 [2nd] **[L1]** [STO▶]
[2nd] **[L3]** [ENTER] [STAT] 1. Compare the lists displayed on the calculator.

Lesson 12-1

12-2 Lesson Reading Guide

Measures of Variation

Get Ready for the Lesson

Read the introduction to Lesson 12-2 in your textbook. Write your answers below.

a. What is the fastest speed?

b. What is the slowest speed?

c. Find the difference between these two speeds.

d. Write a sentence comparing the fastest winning average speed and the slowest winning average speed.

Read the Lesson

Write a definition and give an example of each new vocabulary word or phrase.

Vocabulary	Definition	Example
1. measures of variation		
2. range		
3. quartiles		
4. lower quartile		
5. upper quartile		
6. interquartile range		
7. outlier		

Remember What You Learned

7. Complete the following diagram by filling in the boxes with the appropriate vocabulary words.

Diagram Title:

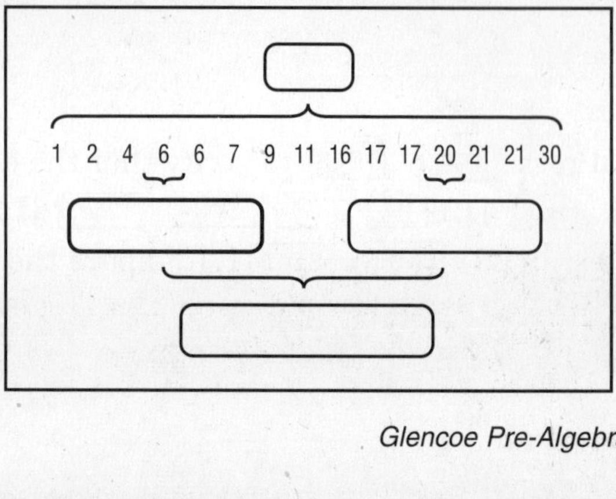

1 2 4 6 6 7 9 11 16 17 17 20 21 21 30

12-2 Study Guide and Intervention

Measures of Variation

The **range** and the **interquartile range** describe how a set of data varies.

Term	Definition
range	The difference between the greatest and the least values of the set
median	The value that separates the data set in half
lower quartile	The median of the lower half of a set of data
upper quartile	The median of the upper half of a set of data
interquartile range	The difference between the upper quartile and the lower quartile
outlier	Data that is more than 1.5 times the value of the interquartile range beyond the quartiles.

Example   Find the range, interquartile range, and any outliers for each set of data.

a. {3, 12, 17, 2, 21, 14, 14, 8}

Step 1 List the data from least to greatest. The range is $21 - 2$ or 19. Then find the median.

2 3 8 12 14 14 17 21

median $= \frac{14 + 12}{2}$ or 13

Step 2 Find the upper and lower quartiles.

2 3 8 12 14 14 17 21

LQ $= \frac{3 + 8}{2}$ median   UQ $= \frac{14 + 17}{2}$
or 5.5   or 15.5

The interquartile range is $15.5 - 5.5$ or 10. There are no outliers.

b.

Stem	Leaf
2	2 6 9
3	1 1 3 4 9
4	0 2 5 5 7 7 8
5	3 4 6 6

$3 \,|\, 4 = 34$

The stem-and-leaf plot displays the data in order. The greatest value is 56. The least value is 22. So, the range is $56 - 22$ or 34.

The median is 42. The LQ is 31 and the UQ is 48. So, the interquartile range is $48 - 31$ or 17.

There are no outliers.

Exercises

WEATHER   For Exercises 1 and 2, use the data in the stem-and-leaf plot at the right.

1. Find the range, median, upper quartile, lower quartile, interquartile range, and any outliers for each set of data.

2. Write a sentence that compares the data.

Average Extreme July Temperatures in World Cities

Low Temps.		High Temps.
9 1 1 0	5	
4	6	4 7 9
9 8 6 5 5 4 3 0 0	7	9
0	8	1 1 3 3 4 8
	9	0 1 2 5
	10	7

$0 \,|\, 8 = 80°F$ $7 \,|\, 9 = 79°F$

Lesson 12-2

12-2 Skills Practice

Measures of Variation

Find the range, interquartile range, and any outliers for each set of data.

1. {7, 9, 21, 8, 13, 19}

2. {33, 34, 27, 40, 38, 35}

3. {37, 29, 42, 33, 31, 36, 40}

4. {87, 72, 104, 94, 85, 71, 80, 98}

5. {92, 89, 124, 114, 98, 118, 115, 106, 101, 149}

6. {6.7, 3.4, 3.8, 4.2, 5.1, 5.8, 6.0, 4.5}

7. {4.3, 1.9, 6.3, 5.1, 2.1, 1.6, 2.4, 5.6, 5.9, 3.5}

8. {127, 58, 49, 101, 104, 98, 189, 111}

9.
Stem	Leaf
1	0 0 3 8 9
2	0 5
3	1 2 4

$2 \mid 0 = 20$

10.
Stem	Leaf
7	8 9
8	1 3 7
9	3 5 6

$9 \mid 3 = 93$

11.
Stem	Leaf
0	2 3 6 8 9
1	2 2 5
2	6
3	2 3 4

$1 \mid 5 = 15$

12.
Stem	Leaf
0	1 1 3 3 7 9
1	2 6 7 8 9 9
2	0 1 2 2 4 5 7 9 9 9
3	2 4 6 7 8
4	0 1 3

$2 \mid 0 = 20$

13.
Stem	Leaf
6	0 6
7	1
8	4 9 9
9	1 3 7 7 7 8

$8 \mid 4 = 84$

14.
Stem	Leaf
4	8
5	1 2 4 7 7
6	0 2 5
7	4

$6 \mid 2 = 62$

HEALTH For Exercises 15–17, use the data in the table showing the calories burned by a 125-pound person.

15. What is the range of the data?

16. What is the interquartile range of the data?

17. Are there any outliers?

18. Which activity burns the most calories per hour? The least calories per hour?

Estimated Calories Burned	
Activity	**Calories Burned per Hour**
Basketball	480
Bicycling	600
Hiking	360
Mowing the Lawn	270
Running	660
Soccer	420
Swimming	600
Weight Training	360
Yoga	240

Source: www.fitresource.com

12-2 Practice

Measures of Variation

Find the range, interquartile range, and any outliers for each set of data.

1. {3, 9, 11, 8, 6, 12, 5, 4}

2. {8, 3, 9, 14, 12, 11, 20, 23, 5, 26}

3. {42, 50, 46, 47, 38, 41}

4. {10.3, 9.8, 10.1, 16.2, 18.0, 11.4, 16.0, 15.8}

5. {107, 82, 93, 112, 120, 95, 98, 56, 109, 110}

6. {106, 103, 112, 109, 115, 118, 113, 108}

7.

Stem	Leaf
1	7 8
2	2 3 5 6 8
3	0

2 | 2 = 22

8.

Stem	Leaf
5	6 7
6	0 1 1 4 8 8 9
7	0 2 3 5 6 7

6 | 1 = 61

9.

Stem	Leaf
4	0 0 0 2 5 7
5	2 6
6	1 8 8
7	0 1 9

5 | 2 = 52

10.

Stem	Leaf
6	4 7 9
7	9
8	1 1 3 3 4 6
9	0 1 2 5

7 | 9 = 79

11.

Stem	Leaf
3	0 1 6 8
4	4
5	2
6	
7	3 3
8	9

5 | 2 = 52

12.

Stem	Leaf
4	3 3 5 7 9
5	0 0 1
6	2
7	4 4 6 8
8	
9	0 1 1 2 2 5

5 | 1 = 51

POPULATION   For Exercises 13–15, use the data in the table at the right.

13. What is the range of populations shown?

14. What is the interquartile range for the annual growth rate?

15. Where does the city with the fastest growth rate fall in terms of population? The city with the slowest growth rate?

Populations of the World's Largest Cities 2000		
City	Population (millions)	Annual Growth Rate (%)
Tokyo, Japan	26.4	0.51
Mexico City, Mexico	18.1	1.81
Mumbai, India	18.1	3.54
Sao Paulo, Brazil	17.8	1.43
New York City, U.S.	16.6	0.37
Lagos, Nigeria	13.4	5.33
Los Angeles, U.S.	13.1	1.15
Calcutta, India	12.9	1.60
Shanghai, China	12.9	−0.35
Buenos Aires, Argentina	12.6	1.14

Source: *World Almanac*

Lesson 12-2

12-2 Word Problem Practice

Measures of Variation

1. SUSPENSION BRIDGES The lengths in meters of the world's largest suspension bridges are given in the table below. Find the range of the data.

Suspension Bridge	Length of center span (meters)
Akashi–Kaikyo Bridge	1991
Great Belt Bridge	1624
Runyang Bridge	1490
Humber Bridge	1410
Jiangyin Suspension Bridge	1385
Tsing Ma Bridge	1377
Verrazano Narrows Bridge	1298
Golden Gate Bridge	1280
Hoga Kusten Bridge	1210
Mackinac Bridge	1158

2. ACADEMICS Mrs. Santiago gave each of her 21 students a reading test. The scores are organized in the stem-and-leaf plot below. Find the median score.

```
Stem | Leaf
  1  | 5 7 8 9
  2  | 0 2 5 5 7 8
  3  | 0 2 5 7 9
  4  | 2 4 5 8 9
  5  | 0
           2|5 5 25
```

3. EXERCISE Shown below is the number of minutes Yashika walked each day for two weeks. Find the upper and lower quartile of the data.

Week 1	25	22	15	30	45	18	25
Week 2	35	42	30	25	20	15	10

4. BASKETBALL Jan tracked the points per game of his favorite basketball player for the 2004–2005 season. During the last six games that he played in the season, he scored these points: 42, 18, 20, 33, 22, 37. Find the upper and lower quartiles, the interquartile range, and determine if there are any outliers.

SPORTS For Exercises 5–7, use the following information.

Rodney researched the longest-playing professional baseball players. He made a table of the nine who have played professional baseball for 25 seasons or more.

Player	Years Played
Eddie Collins	25
Cap Anson	27
Jim Kaat	25
Bobby Wallace	25
Tommy John	26
Charlie Hough	27
Rickey Henderson	25
Deacon McGuire	26
Nolan Ryan	27

Source: www.baseballreference.com

5. Find the range of the data set.

6. What is the median of the data set?

7. Find the upper and lower quartile and the interquartile range.

12-2 Enrichment

Variance

Another way to measure the variation of a set of data is by computing the **variance**. The higher the variance is for a group of numbers, the more "spread out" the data will be.

The table below shows the price of the stock for two companies during one week.

	Monday	Tuesday	Wednesday	Thursday	Friday
Acme Computer Systems	$10	$7	$3	$8	$12
Baker Pencil Company	$7	$8	$7	$9	$9

Computing the variance will show which company's stock has the greater variation. To compute the variance, follow these steps:

Step 1   Subtract the mean from each number in the set.

Step 2   Multiply each difference in step 1 by itself.

Step 3   Add these differences.

Step 4   Divide the total by the number of members of the set.

Example   **Find the variance for Acme Computer Systems.**

The mean average price for the week for each company is $8

$$(10 - 8) \times (10 - 8) + (7 - 8) \times (7 - 8) + (3 - 8) \times (3 - 8) + (8 - 8) \times (8 - 8) + (12 - 8) \times (12 - 8)$$

$$4 \quad + \quad 1 \quad + \quad 25 \quad + \quad 0 \quad + \quad 16 \quad = 46$$

The variance is $46 \div 5$, or 9.2.

Exercises

Solve.

1. Do you think the variance for Baker Pencil Company will be higher than the variance for Acme Computer Systems? Why? Compute the variance for Baker Pencil Company to see whether you are correct.

2. Consolidated Airlines also had an average price last week of $8 per share, but its variance was 10.8. Indicate five stock prices that could produce this variance. (*Hint:* Change only the Monday and Tuesday prices for Acme.)

3. Sleepy Mattress Company's stock had an average price last week of $8 per share and a variance of 0. What was the price of shares each day last week?

4. Are there any values that the variance cannot equal? If so, what are these values?

12-3 Lesson Reading Guide

Box-and-Whisker Plots

Get Ready for the Lesson

Read the introduction to Lesson 12-3 in your textbook. Write your answers below.

a. Find the low, high, and the median temperature, and the upper and lower quartile for each city.

	Low	LQ	Median	UQ	High
Tampa, FL					
Caribou, ME					

b. Draw a number line extending from 0 to 85. Label every 5 units.

c. About one-half inch above the number line, plot the data found in part **a** for Tampa. About three-fourths inch above the number line, plot the data for Caribou.

d. Write a few sentences comparing the average monthly temperatures.

Read the Lesson

Write a definition and give an example for the new vocabulary phrase.

Vocabulary	Definition	Example
1. box-and-whisker plot		

Remember What You Learned

2. Complete the following concept map of how to make a box-and-whisker plot.

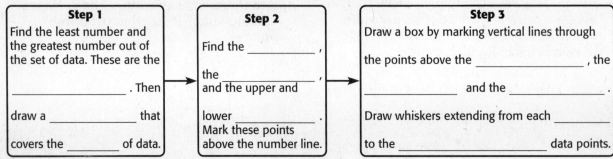

Step 1
Find the least number and the greatest number out of the set of data. These are the _____ . Then draw a _____ that covers the _____ of data.

Step 2
Find the _____ , the _____ , and the upper and lower _____ . Mark these points above the number line.

Step 3
Draw a box by marking vertical lines through the points above the _____ , the _____ and the _____ . Draw whiskers extending from each _____ to the _____ data points.

12-3 Study Guide and Intervention

Box-and-Whisker Plots

Box-and-Whisker Plot	**Words**	A **box and whisker plot** divides a set of data into four parts using the median and quartiles. Each of these parts contains 25% of the data.
	Model	

Example 1   FOOD   The heat levels of popular chile peppers are shown in the table. Display the data in a box-and-whisker plot.

Step 1 Find the least and greatest number. Then draw a number line that covers the range of the data.

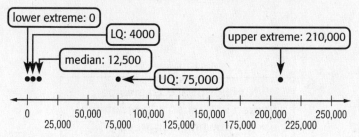

Step 2 Mark the median, the extremes, and the quartiles. Mark these points above the number line.

Step 3 Draw a box and the whiskers.

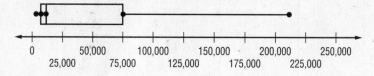

Heat Level of Chile Peppers	
Name	**Heat Level***
Aji escabeche	17,000
Bell	0
Cayenne	8,000
Habañero	210,000
Jalapeño	25,000
Mulato	1,000
New Mexico	4,500
Pasilla	5,500
Serrano	4,000
Tabasco	120,000
Tepín	75,000
Thai hot	60,000

Source: Chile Pepper Institute
*Scoville heat units

Lesson 12-3

Exercises

Draw a box-and-whisker plot for each set of data.

1. {17, 5, 28, 33, 25, 5, 12, 3, 16, 11, 22, 31, 9, 11}

2. {$21, $50, $78, $13, $45, $5, $12, $37, $61, $11, $77, $31, $19, $11, $29, $16}

12-3 Skills Practice

Box-and-Whisker Plots

Draw a box-and-whisker plot for each set of data.

1. {6, 9, 22, 17, 14, 11, 18, 28, 19, 21, 16, 15, 12, 3}

2. {$45, $37, $50, $53, $61, $95, $46, $40, $48, $62}

3. {14, 9, 1, 16, 20, 17, 18, 11, 15}

4. {$20, $35, $42, $26, $53, $18, $36, $27, $21, $32}

5. {97, 83, 100, 99, 102, 104, 97, 101, 115, 106, 94, 108, 102, 100, 109, 103, 102, 98, 108}

6. {188, 203, 190, 212, 214, 217, 174, 220, 219, 211, 201, 210, 214, 217, 213, 204, 187, 206, 210}

7.

Goals Scored by MLS Leading Scorers, 2000		
26	15	12
16	15	1
18	11	10
16	15	5
16	13	9

Source: *World Almanac*

8.

Number of 300 Games per Person in Women's International Bowling Congress		
12	17	23
21	17	23
14	21	12
17	19	24
18	27	13
14	20	12
16	12	16

Source: *World Almanac*

12-3 Practice

Box-and-Whisker Plots

Draw a box-and-whisker plot for each set of data.

1. {14, 30, 35, 8, 29, 28, 31, 42, 20, 36, 32}

2. {$105, $98, $83, $127, $115, $114, $132, $93, $107, $101, $119}

3. {211, 229, 196, 230, 240, 212, 231, 233, 243, 214, 239, 238, 228, 237, 230, 234, 239, 240, 212, 232, 239, 240, 237}

4. {3.7, 6.2, 4.1, 2.4, 1.0, 1.5, 1.4, 2.1, 2.6, 3.0, 1.3, 1.7}

For Exercises 5–7, use the box-and-whisker plot shown.

5. How tall is the highest peak of the Hindu Kush?

6. What is the median height of the major peaks?

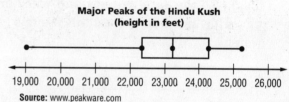

Major Peaks of the Hindu Kush
(height in feet)

19,000 20,000 21,000 22,000 23,000 24,000 25,000 26,000

Source: www.peakware.com

7. Write a sentence describing what the box-and-whisker plot tells about the major peaks of the Hindu Kush.

For Exercises 8–10, use the box-and-whisker plot shown.

8. In which year was the corn yield more varied? Explain.

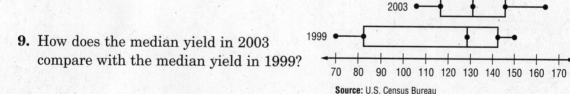

Corn Yield by State
(bushels per acre)

2003

1999

70 80 90 100 110 120 130 140 150 160 170

Source: U.S. Census Bureau

9. How does the median yield in 2003 compare with the median yield in 1999?

10. Write a few sentences that compare the 1999 yields with the 2003 yields.

Lesson 12-3

12-3 Word Problem Practice

Box-and-Whisker Plots

1. **CARS** Martina bought a new car and wanted to know how many miles per gallon her new car got. She kept track of her mileage and gas consumption for 10 separate trips. The miles per gallon are displayed in the box-and-whisker plot below. What is the median of the data?

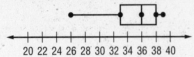

2. **ZOOLOGY** Archie researched pandas for a science project. He looked up the weight in kilograms of adult pandas and displayed the data in a box-and-whisker plot. How much do most adult pandas weigh?

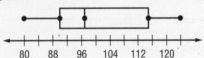

3. **SPORTS** The number of games won by the teams in each conference of the National Basketball League is displayed below. Write a few sentences that compare the data.

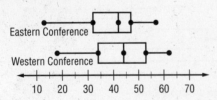

4. **FOOD** The table shows the recent top 10 ice cream-consuming countries. Make a box-and-whisker plot of the data.

Country	Consumption per Capita (pints)
Australia	36.8
New Zealand	27.8
USA	27.5
Sweden	23.8
Canada	22.2
Ireland	20.6
Norway	20.2
Finland	19.4
Denmark	16.9
Germany	16.7

WEATHER For Exercises 5–7, use the information below.

George researched peak wind gusts in Texas. He made a box-and-whisker plot to display the data he collected.

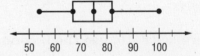

5. What is the slowest recorded wind gust?

6. What percent of the wind gusts range from 67 to 82 miles per hour?

7. What would a peak gust have to be for it to be an outlier?

12-3 Enrichment

Traffic Safety Facts

Primary enforcement seatbelt laws allow law enforcement officers to pull over drivers and ticket them for not wearing a seatbelt as they would for any other violation. Secondary seatbelt laws allow the driver to be ticketed for not wearing a seatbelt only if they are stopped for another violation of the law. The table to the right lists several states with seat belt laws and the estimated seatbelt use rates.

Type of Safety Belt Law	State	Seatbelt Use Rate (%)
Primary	Texas	76.1
Primary	Oklahoma	67.9
Secondary	Arkansas	54.5
Primary	Louisiana	68.1
Secondary	Nevada	74.5
Primary	California	91.1
Primary	Hawaii	82.5

Source: National Highway Traffic Safety Administration

1. Make a box-and-whisker plot of the seatbelt use rates.

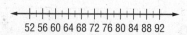

   52 56 60 64 68 72 76 80 84 88 92

   a. What are the upper and lower quartiles?

   b. What is the median seatbelt use rate?

2. Make a back-to-back stem-and-leaf plot to compare the seatbelt use rates in states with primary seatbelt laws to those states with secondary seat belt laws.

3. What conclusion can you make from the plot in Exercise 2?

Lesson 12-3

12-4 Lesson Reading Guide

Histograms

Get Ready for the Lesson

Read the introduction to Lesson 12-4 in your textbook. Write your answers below.

a. What does each tally mark represent?

b. What does the last column represent?

c. What do you notice about the intervals that represent the counties?

Read the Lesson

Write a definition and give an example of the new vocabulary word.

Vocabulary	Definition	Example
1. histogram		

Complete the following statements about frequency tables and histograms.

2. If the first frequency interval goes from 1 to 50, the next frequency interval goes from _____.

3. Because the intervals in a histogram are _____, all of the bars have the _____.

4. In a histogram, there is _____ bars.

5. Intervals that have a frequency of 0 have _____.

6. The height of a bar in a histogram corresponds to the _____ of the data for that _____.

Remember What You Learned

7. Label the following in the histogram at right: interval, frequency, bar, and histogram. Then make a frequency table showing the same information as the histogram.

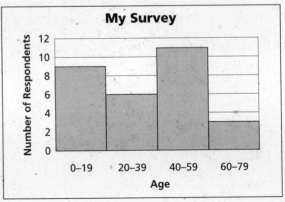

12-4 Study Guide and Intervention

Histograms

Histograms	A histogram uses bars to display numerical data that have been organized into equal intervals. • There is no space between bars. • Because the intervals are equal, all of the bars have the same width. • Intervals with a frequency of 0 have no bar.

Example **ELEVATIONS** The frequency table shows the highest elevations in each state. Display the data in a histogram.

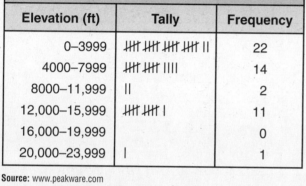

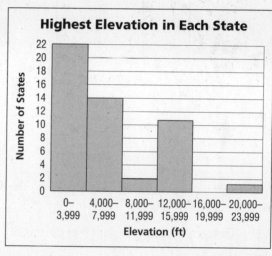

Source: www.peakware.com

Step 1 Draw and label the axes as shown. Include the title.

Step 2 Show the frequency intervals on the horizontal axis and an interval of 2 on the vertical axis.

Step 3 For each elevation interval, draw a bar whose height is given by the frequency.

Exercises

For Exercises 1–3, use the information shown in the table below.

1. The frequency table shows voter participation in 2000. Display the data in a histogram.

Voter Participation by State (2000)		
Percent voting	**Tally**	**Frequency**
35–39	I	1
40–44		0
45–49	ЖHТ I	6
50–54	ЖHТ ЖHТ II	12
55–59	ЖHТ ЖHТ III	13
60–64	ЖHТ ЖHТ II	12
65–69	ЖHТ I	6

2. How many states had a voter turnout greater than 50 percent?

Source: U.S. Census Bureau

3. How many states had fewer than 40 percent voting?

Lesson 12-4

12-4 Skills Practice

Histograms

Display each set of data in a histogram.

1.

Shots per Hockey Game		
Number of Shots	Tally	Frequency
1–7	ℍℍ	5
8–14	I	1
15–21	ℍℍ III	8
22–28	II	2
29–35	IIII	4

2.

Employees in Each Office		
Number of Employees	Tally	Frequency
10–19	II	2
20–29	ℍℍ I	6
30–39	ℍℍ IIII	9
40–49	ℍℍ III	8
50–59	I	1

3.

Basketball Backboards on Each Playground		
Number of Backboards	Tally	Frequency
0–4	ℍℍ ℍℍ ℍℍ I	16
5–9	III	3
10–14	ℍℍ III	8
15–19	ℍℍ ℍℍ I	11
20–24		0
25–29	IIII	4

4.

Population of Loons on Local Lakes		
Number of Loons	Tally	Frequency
30–39	II	2
40–49		0
50–59	ℍℍ I	6
60–69	ℍℍ IIII	9
70–79	ℍℍ ℍℍ ℍℍ II	17
80–89	IIII	4

12-4 Practice

Histograms

Display each set of data in a histogram.

1.

Ages of Zoo Volunteers		
Age	Tally	Frequency
18–27	III	3
28–37	HHT III	8
38–47	HHT HHT HHT I	16
48–57	HHT II	12
58–67	HHT	5
68–77	II	2

2.

Crossword Puzzle Solving Times		
Time (min)	Tally	Frequency
0–4	III	3
5–9	I	1
10–14	HHT I	6
15–19	HHT HHT IIII	14
20–24		0
25–29	II	2

For Exercises 3–6, use the histogram at the right.

3. What size are the intervals?

4. How many countries have nine or fewer threatened species?

5. Which interval contains the median number of endangered species?

6. Can you tell from the histogram whether any of the countries have zero threatened species? Explain.

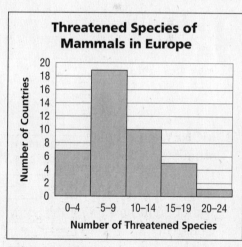

Threatened Species of Mammals in Europe

Source: www.redlist.org

12-4 Word Problem Practice

Histograms

1. MUSIC Students in grades 6–12 were asked, "Of the songs you listen to, what percent of the songs' lyrics do you know?" The histogram shows the results. How many students responded in all?

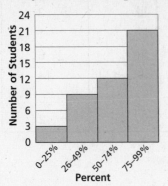

2. VOLUNTEERING The histogram shows how many hours per year a group of teens said they spend volunteering. How many hours did most of them volunteer?

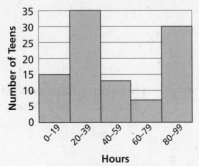

3. MONEY A group of students were asked How much cash (in bills) is in your wallet right now? Construct a histogram to represent the data.

Amount	Number of Students
0-$9	54
$10-$19	20
$20-$29	16
$30-$39	5
$40-$49	4
$50-$59	1

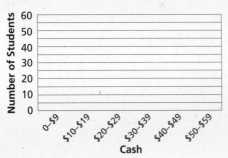

4. WEATHER The list below shows the highest recorded temperature of the 20 largest U.S. cities. Display the data in a histogram.

122	110	111	106	109
105	104	104	105	102
104	106	102	104	108
112	113	109	111	103

NEWSPAPERS For Exercises 5 and 6, use the histogram below.
Teens ages 13 to 18 who read a newspaper at least once a week were asked How many minutes a day, on average, do you spend reading the newspaper? The responses are displayed in the histogram.

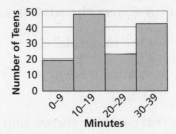

5. How many teens said they read a newspaper for less than 30 minutes?

6. How many teens were surveyed in all?

12-4 Enrichment

Displaying Real-World Data

The Big D Marathon is an annual event that takes place in Dallas, Texas, in the spring. Marathons are 26.2 miles in length and require intense preparation and endurance. Here are the results from the 50-54 age group from the April 3, 2005, Big D Marathon. 3:58:08 means 3 hours, 58 minutes, 8 seconds.

Place	Name	Age	Time (h:min:s)
1	Kathy Johnson	50	3:58:08
2	Lana Parks	51	4:17:16
3	Adrienne Gabriel	50	4:55:33
4	Sarah Gordon	50	5:07:45
5	Teresa Lynd	52	5:22:03
6	Margaret Darneille	53	5:25:56
7	Deborah Kerr-Leathem	51	5:34:36
8	Veleria Cowsen	54	6:03:29
9	Kathy Davidson	50	6:15:50

Source: www.texasmarathon.com

1. Use the data to complete the frequency table below. Then draw a histogram to display the data. Number of Runners in Each Time Group

Time (in hours)	Tally	Frequency
3:00 – 3:59		
4:00 – 4:59		
5:00 – 5:59		
6:00 – 6:59		

2. Draw a stem-and-leaf plot to display the data for the times at which the runners completed the marathon.

Hours	Minutes

3. Draw a box-and-whiskers plot to display the times data.

3:50 4:10 4:30 4:50 5:10 5:30 5:50 6:10 6:30

4. What is the median time that this group of runners finished the marathon?

Lesson 12-4

12-4 Spreadsheet Activity

Histograms

Example Use a spreadsheet to make a histogram of the data on home runs.

Major League Baseball Home Runs in the 2001 Season							
Team	Home Runs	Team	Home Runs	Team	Home Runs	Team	Home Runs
Rangers	246	Dodgers	206	Braves	174	Royals	152
Giants	235	Yankees	203	Mariners	169	Mets	147
White Sox	214	Athletics	199	Marlins	166	Tigers	139
Rockies	213	Cardinals	199	Twins	164	Orioles	136
Indians	212	Red Sox	198	Phillies	164	Expos	131
Brewers	209	Blue Jays	195	Pirates	161	Devil Rays	121
Diamondbacks	208	Cubs	194	Padres	161		
Astros	208	Reds	176	Angels	158		

Source: *MLB Advanced Media*

Step 1 Enter the numbers of home runs into Column A. Enter the measurement classes into Column B. In this case, classes of 120, 130, 140, and so on, are appropriate.

Step 2 Choose Histogram from the Data Analysis menu on the Tools menu. Note that you may have to add this option if it is not already installed.

Step 3 In the Histogram dialog box, choose Column A for the Input Range and Column B for the Bin Range. Check the Chart Output box to have the computer sort the data and create the histogram. Click OK.

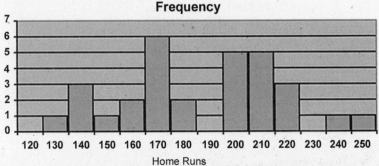

The spreadsheet will allow you to change the appearance of the graph by adding titles and axis labels, adjusting the scales on the axes, changing colors, and so on.

Exercises

1. Use a spreadsheet program to create a histogram of the home run data using measurement classes of 20.

2. Use the Internet or other reference to find some data on a subject of your choice. Create a histogram of the data.

12-5 Lesson Reading Guide

Selecting an Appropriate Display

Get Ready for the Lesson

Read the introduction to Lesson 12-5 in your textbook. Write your answers below.

a. What type of graph can be used to display the data?

b. Find another way to display the data that shows the number of items divided into specific categories. Draw the graph and describe how you named your categories.

c. Find a third way to display the data that shows how they are spread out. Draw the graph.

Read the Lesson

Complete the following statements by filling in the blanks with the following words.

circle graph   bar graph   box-and-whisker plot
frequency table   histogram   line graph

1. The best time to use a _____ is when you would like to display the frequency of data using bars.

2. If you would like to compare the number of values in certain intervals, it is best to use a _____ . If you would like to display this data, it is best to use a

_____ .

3. If you would like to divide a set into four parts using the median and quartiles, a

_____ would be the best way to display the data.

4. To show changes over a period of time, you should display the data in a _____ .

5. To compare parts of data to the whole, you should display the data in a _____ .

Remember What You Learned

6. Think of an example of a set of data you have seen in an earlier lesson. Explain what the benefits or drawbacks might be for using each of the possible data displays.

12-5 Study Guide and Intervention

Selecting an Appropriate Display

CHOOSE APPROPRIATE DISPLAYS Data can be visually represented in many different ways, including bar graphs, box-and-whisker plots, circle graphs, frequency tables, histograms, line graphs, line plots, stem-and-leaf plots, tables, and Venn diagrams.

Example **HOUSING** The table shows the total number of houses occupied in the U.S. from 1980–2003. Choose an appropriate type of display for this situation. Then make the display.

Year	1980	1985	1990	1995	2000	2001	2002	2003
Total Housing	79,638	87,887	94,224	99,985	105,720	107,010	104,965	105,560

The data can be represented in two ways. First, you can use a bar graph showing the number in each year. Second, you can use a line graph to show the change from 1980 to 2003.

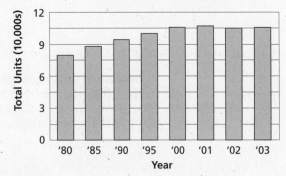
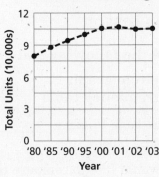

Exercise

Choose an appropriate type of display for the data set. Then make the display.

Player	Points Per Game
Allen Iverson	33.2
LeBron James	30.7
Gilbert Arenas	29.1
Dwyane Wade	27.7
Paul Pierce	27.1

Source: espn.com

12-5 Skills Practice

Selecting an Appropriate Display

Choose an appropriate style of display for each data set. Justify your choice.

1. the life span of various types of fish

2. the number of teachers for 5 different high schools

3. the number of students who are in a band, science club, and/or student council

4. the names of the Nobel prize winners for the past 50 years

5. the total rainfall for several 100-day time intervals

6. **PARTY** A class of 26 students voted on which type of snack they would like to have at their class party. 13 students voted for brownies, 7 voted for ice cream, 5 voted for cookies, and 2 voted for pretzels. Which graph best represents this situaton?

A.   **Snack Preference Votes**

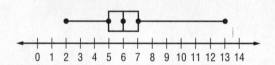

B.

Snack	Frequency
Brownies	⌗⌗ ⌗⌗ III
Ice Cream	⌗⌗ II
Cookies	⌗⌗
Pretzels	II

C.   **Snack Preference**

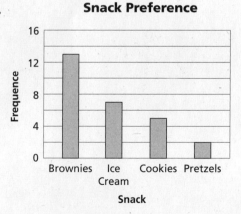

D.   **Snack Preference**

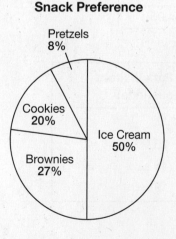

Lesson 12-5

12-5 Practice

Selecting an Appropriate Display

Choose an appropriate style of display for each data set. Justify your choice.

1. the monthly price of apples over a two year period.

2. results of a poll of 30 students favorite type of candy

3. the income of the middle 50% of U.S. households

4. the number of terms served by current senators

5. the number of runners who finished a marathon in each ten-minute interval

Choose an appropriate style of display for each data set. Then make a display.

6. Winning times for the 200-Meter backstroke event at the Olympics.

Year	Winning Time
1976	1:59.19
1980	2:01.93
1984	2:00.23
1988	1:59.37
1992	1:58.47
1996	1:58.54
2000	1:56.76
2004	1:54.95

Source: *World Almanac*

7.

Monthly Park Visitors (in thousands)		
6	7	12
15	25	40
46	46	37
22	19	8

12-5 Word Problem Practice

Selecting an Appropriate Display

1. RADIO The table below shows the average amount of time that teenagers spent listening to the radio from 1999 to 2003. What would be an appropriate way to display the data?

Year	1999	2000	2001	2002	2003
Hours/week	11.4	10.5	10.0	9.25	8.5

2. TELEVISION The table below shows the number of hours students spend watching TV in one week. What would be an appropriate way to display the data?

Students	1-10	11-20	21-30	31-40	40+
Hours	6	19	14	4	1

3. ENTERTAINMENT Teens spend more time on the Internet than with any other form of media. In an average week, they spend 16.7 hours online versus 13.6 hours watching TV, and 12 hours listening to the radio. Display the data using the most appropriate display.

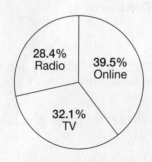

4. MONEY MATTERS The table below shows the minimum age that a person must be in order to obtain a full driver's license. Would a box-and-whisker plot be an appropriate display of the data set? Explain.

State	CT	GA	ID	NJ	TX
Minimum age (yr, mo)	16, 6	18,0	15,0	17,0	16,0

Source: http://golocalnet.com/drivingage/

VIDEO GAMES For Exercises 5-7, use the information below.
The table shows some of the recent top selling video game categories.

Genre	Percent
Action	30.1%
Children	9.5%
Racing	9.4%
Simulation	9.0%
Sports	17.8%

Source: www.theesa.com/archives

5. What type of graph would best represents the data if each category is to be compared to the whole?

6. What type of graph would best represents the data if the categories are to be compared to each other?

7. Suppose you wanted to compare how the percent of action games had changed over the last 5 years. What type of graph would best represent the situation?

Lesson 12-5

12-5 Enrichment

Statistical Graphs

Bar graphs and pictographs are used to compare quantities. Line graphs are used to show changes. Circle graphs compare parts to parts, or parts to the whole.

Solve. Use the pictograph.

Principal Languages of the World
(to nearest fifty million)

English	웃웃웃웃
Hindi	웃웃ᠶ
Arabic	웃ᠶ
Portuguese	웃ᠶ
Chinese	웃웃웃웃웃웃웃ᠶ
Russian	웃웃ᠶ
Spanish	웃웃ᠶ
French	웃
Bengali	웃ᠶ

웃 = 100 million

1. How many people speak Portuguese?

2. What is the ratio of people who speak Spanish to those who speak Russian?

3. What three languages are each spoken by about 150 million people?

4. How many fewer people speak Arabic than Hindi?

Solve. Use the circle graph.

5. Which continent has the smallest population?

6. How does the population of South America compare to that of Africa?

7. What is the population of Australia if the world's population is about 6 billion?

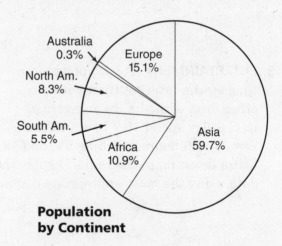

Population by Continent

Solve. Use the line graph.

8. During which ten-year period was the increase in the price of eggs greatest?

9. What was the price of a dozen eggs in 1940?

10. What was the percent of increase in the price of eggs from 1940 to 1950?

11. What was the increase in cents from 1930 to 1980?

12-6 Lesson Reading Guide
Misleading Graphs

Get Ready for the Lesson

Read the introduction to Lesson 12-6 in your textbook. Write your answers below.

a. Do both graphs show the same information?

b. Which graph suggests a dramatic increase in sales from May to June?

c. Which graph suggests steady sales?

d. How are the graphs similar? How are they different?

Reading the Lesson

Complete the following statements by filling in the blanks with the following words.

different	gradually	horizontal	interval(s)
label(s)	rapidly	title(s)	vertical

1. If two graphs showing the same information have different vertical scales, that means that on the _____ axis, the _____ are different.

2. If two graphs showing the same information have different horizontal scales, that means that on the _____ axis, the intervals are _____ .

3. A graph can be misleading if it has no_____ or if it has no_____ on the scales.

4. If a graph shows steady change, the plotted values should increase or decrease _____ .

5. If a graph shows dramatic change, the plotted values should increase or decrease _____ .

Remember What You Learned

6. Use a dictionary and a book of synonyms to rewrite the following sentence by replacing the underlined words with ones you are more familiar with.

Statistics or statistical graphs can be misleading when the same data are represented in different ways, so that each graph gives a different visual impression.

12-6 Study Guide and Intervention

Misleading Graphs

Example The graphs below show the increase in the number of events held in the Summer Olympics from 1948 to 1996.

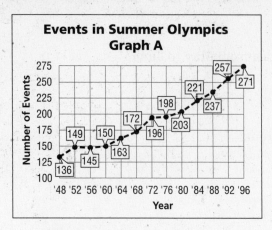
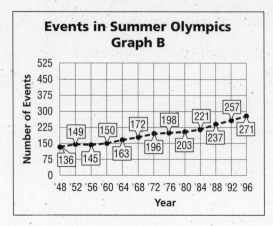

a. What causes the graphs to differ in their appearance?

Different vertical scales and the lack of a zero on Graph A's axis result in different visual impressions.

b. Which graph appears to show a more rapid increase in the number of events held in the Summer Olympics? Explain.

Graph A; the steeper slope of the line and the higher position of the line relative to the scale make it appear that the number of events is greater and increasing faster.

Exercises

For Exercises 1–3, refer to the graphs below.

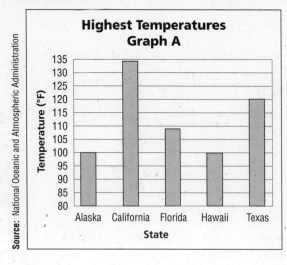
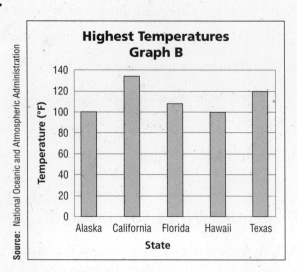

1. What is the highest recorded temperature in California? In Alaska?

2. In which graph does the difference between these two temperatures appear to be minimized?

3. How do the graphs create different appearances?

12-6 Skills Practice

Misleading Graphs

For Exercises 1–3, refer to the graphs below.

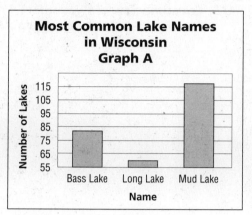

Source: Wisconsin Department of Natural Resources

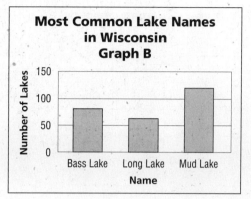

Source: Wisconsin Department of Natural Resources

1. How many lakes in Wisconsin are named Bass Lake? Long Lake? Mud Lake?

2. Which graph gives the impression that only a few lakes are called Long Lake, while numerous lakes are called Bass Lake?

3. What causes the graphs to differ in their appearance?

For Exercises 4–6, refer to the graphs below.

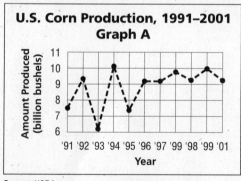

Source: USDA

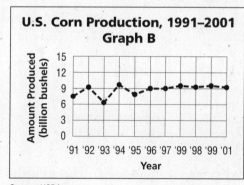

Source: USDA

4. Do these graphs show the same information?

5. Which graph suggests that U.S. corn production is relatively stable?

6. What causes the graphs to differ in their appearance?

12-6 Practice

Misleading Graphs

For Exercises 1–3, refer to the graphs below.

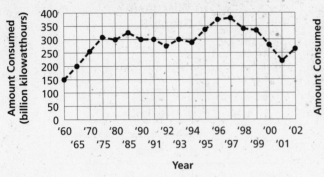

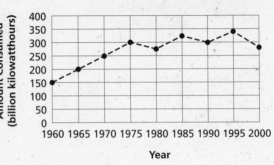

1. What was the U.S. consumption of hydroelectric power in 1990?

2. Which graph gives the impression that the use of hydroelectric power in the United States has experienced many dips as well as rises between 1975 and 2002?

3. What causes the graphs to differ in their appearance?

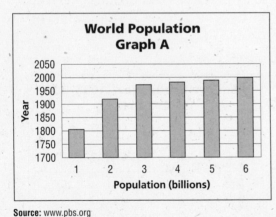

Source: www.pbs.org

Source: www.pbs.org

For Exercises 4–6, refer to the graphs below.

4. What was the world's population in 1999?

5. Which graph gives the impression that the world's population skyrocketed between 1800 and 1925? Explain.

6. Are the vertical axis and the horizontal axis in either graph misleading? Explain.

12-6 Word Problem Practice

Misleading Graphs

1. **TELEPHONE SERVICE** A market research company was hired to track the market share of AllTalk, a long-distance carrier, from 2003 to 2006. Which graph shows a more dramatic increase?

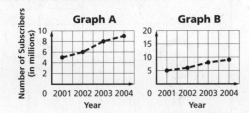

2. **HOUSING** The graphs below show the median sales price of new single-family homes sold in the United States in 1990 and 2000. Explain why the graphs look different.

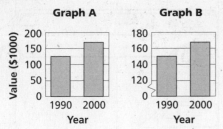

3. **POSTAL RATES** Emma wants to graph postal rates from 1981 to 2005.

1981	1985	1988	1991	1995	1999	2002	2005
20¢	22¢	25¢	29¢	32¢	33¢	34¢	37¢

Source: http://www.vaughns-1-pagers.com/economics/postal-rates.htm

In her graph, she wants to exaggerate the increases. How can she show this?

4. **MARKETING** The graph below displays the results of a taste test of different colas. The graph suggests that cola B was the overwhelming favorite. Is this statement accurate? Explain.

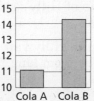

TASTE TESTS For Exercises 5 and 6, use the graphs below.
Tasty Chicken Restaurant wanted to find out which chicken strips people prefer. The restaurant offered three kinds of chicken strips to taste. The results are displayed in the graphs below.

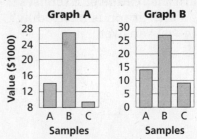

5. Do both graphs show the same information?

6. Which graph suggests that choice B was preferred three to one?

12-6 Enrichment

Using and Misusing Graphs

Refer to the graphs at the right.

1. Do Graphs A and B give the same information on sales?

2. Find the ratio of Hilly's sales to Valley's sales.

3. In Graph A, the Hilly van is about 2.5 cm high by 6 cm long. What is its area?

4. The Valley van is about 0.75 cm high by 2 cm long. What is its area?

5. In Graph B, both vans are about 1.5 cm high. The Hilly van is about 6 cm long. What is its area?

6. The Valley van is about 2 cm long. What is its area?

7. Compute the following ratios.

   Graph A: $\dfrac{\text{Area of Hilly}}{\text{Area of Valley}}$

   Graph B: $\dfrac{\text{Area of Hilly}}{\text{Area of Valley}}$

8. Compare the results of Exercises 2 and 7. Which graph is misleading? Explain your answer.

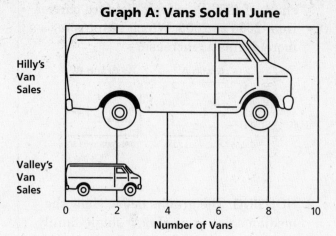

Graph A: Vans Sold In June

Hilly's Van Sales

Valley's Van Sales

Number of Vans

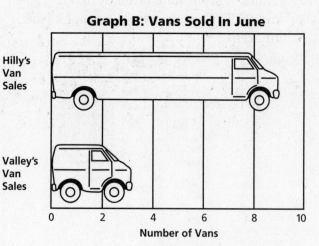

Graph B: Vans Sold In June

Hilly's Van Sales

Valley's Van Sales

Number of Vans

Use Graphs C and D to answer each question.

9. Which graph is easier to read?

10. Compare the vertical scales. How do they differ?

11. Which graph gives a better impression of the trend in sales? Explain.

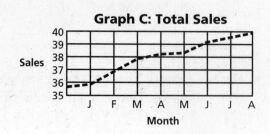

Graph C: Total Sales

Sales

Month

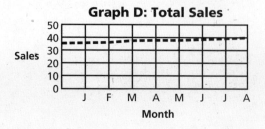

Graph D: Total Sales

Sales

Month

12-7 Lesson Reading Guide

Simple Probability

Get Ready for the Lesson

Read the introduction to Lesson 12-7 in your textbook. Write your answers below.

a. Write the ratio that compares the number of tiles labeled E to the total number of tiles.

b. What percent of the tiles are labeled E?

c. What fraction of tiles is this?

d. Suppose a player chooses a tile. Is there a better chance of choosing a D or an N? Explain.

Read the Lesson

Write a definition and give an example of each new vocabulary word or phrase.

Vocabulary	Definition	Example
1. outcomes		
2. simple event		
3. probability		
4. sample space		
5. theoretical probability		
6. experimental probability		

Remember What You Learned

7. Look up *theoretical* and *experimental* in the dictionary. How can their definitions help you remember the difference between theoretical probability and experimental probability?

12-7 Study Guide and Intervention

Simple Probability

Probability is the chance some event will happen.

$$P(\text{event}) = \frac{(\text{number of favorable outcomes})}{(\text{number of possible outcomes})}$$

Example A bag contains 6 red marbles, 1 blue marble, and 3 yellow marbles. One marble is selected at random. Find the probability of each outcome.

a. P(yellow)

$$P(\text{event}) = \frac{(\text{number of favorable outcomes})}{(\text{number of possible outcomes})}$$

$$= \frac{3}{10} \text{ or } 30\%$$

There is a 30% chance of choosing a yellow marble.

b. P(blue or yellow)

$$P(\text{event}) = \frac{(\text{number of favorable outcomes})}{(\text{number of possible outcomes})}$$

$$= \frac{(1+3)}{10} = \frac{4}{10} \text{ or } 40\%$$

There is a 40% chance of choosing a blue or yellow marble.

c. P(red, blue, or yellow)

$$P(\text{event}) = \frac{(\text{number of favorable outcomes})}{(\text{number of possible outcomes})}$$

$$= \frac{(6+1+3)}{10} = \frac{10}{10} \text{ or } 100\%$$

There is a 100% chance of choosing a red, blue, or yellow marble.

d. P(black)

$$P(\text{event}) = \frac{(\text{number of favorable outcomes})}{(\text{number of possible outcomes})}$$

$$= \frac{0}{10} \text{ or } 0\%$$

There is a 0% chance of choosing a black marble.

Exercises

A bag contains 5 red marbles, 5 blue marbles, 6 green marbles, 8 purple marbles, and 1 white marble. One is selected at random. Find the probability of each outcome. Express each probability as a fraction and as a percent.

1. $P(\text{white})$

2. $P(\text{red})$

3. $P(\text{green})$

4. $P(\text{purple})$

5. $P(\text{white, blue, or green})$

6. $P(\text{red or blue})$

7. $P(\text{red or purple})$

8. $P(\text{green or purple})$

9. $P(\text{green, purple, or white})$

10. $P(\text{red, blue, green, purple, or white})$

11. $P(\text{red, blue, or purple})$

Skills Practice

Simple Probability

A spinner like the one shown is used in a game.
Determine the probability of each outcome if
the spinner is equally likely to land on each
section. Express each probability as a fraction
and as a percent.

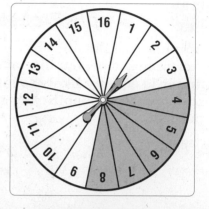

1. $P(10)$

2. $P(\text{odd})$

3. $P(\text{greater than } 7)$

4. $P(\text{prime})$

5. $P(1 \text{ or } 2)$

6. $P(\text{less than } 5)$

7. $P(\text{Shaded})$

8. $P(\text{Not shaded})$

There are 4 red marbles, 1 blue marble, 9 green marbles, and 6 yellow marble in
a bag. Suppose one marble is selected at random. Find the probability of each
outcome. Express each probability as a fraction and as a percent.

9. $P(\text{red})$

10. $P(\text{blue})$

11. $P(\text{yellow})$

12. $P(\text{red or blue})$

13. $P(\text{white})$

14. $P(\text{red, blue, or green})$

Suppose two 1–6 number cubes are rolled. Find the probability of each outcome.
Express each probability as a fraction and as a percent. (*Hint:* Make a table to
show the sample space as in Example 2.) Round to the nearest tenth, if necessary.

15. $P(3 \text{ or } 5)$

16. $P(\text{both even})$

17. $P(\text{odd product})$

18. $P(\text{sum more than } 10)$

19. $P(\text{both the same})$

20. $P(\text{product is a square})$

Lesson 12-7

12-7 Practice

Simple Probability

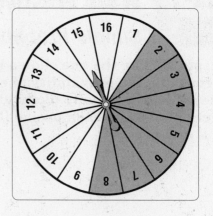

A spinner like the one shown is used in a game. Determine the probability of each outcome if the spinner is equally likely to land on each section. Express each probability as a fraction and as a percent.

1. $P(15)$

2. $P(\text{even})$

3. $P(\text{greater than 10})$

4. $P(\text{perfect square})$

5. $P(1 \text{ or } 2)$

6. $P(\text{less than 9})$

7. $P(\text{not shaded})$

8. $P(\text{shaded})$

There are 8 red marbles, 5 blue marbles, 11 green marbles, and 1 yellow marble in a bag. Suppose one marble is selected at random. Find the probability of each outcome. Express each probability as a fraction and as a percent.

9. $P(\text{red})$

10. $P(\text{blue})$

11. $P(\text{yellow})$

12. $P(\text{red or blue})$

13. $P(\text{black})$

14. $P(\text{red, blue, or green})$

Suppose two 1–6 number cubes are rolled. Find the probability of each outcome. Express each probability as a fraction and as a percent. (*Hint:* Make a table to show the sample space as in Example 2.) Round to the nearest tenth if necessary.

15. $P(1 \text{ or } 5)$

16. $P(\text{both odd})$

17. $P(\text{even product})$

18. $P(\text{sum more than 8})$

19. $P(\text{both different})$

20. $P(\text{sum is a square})$

21. To the nearest tenth of a percent, what is the probability that today is a weekday?

12-7 Word Problem Practice

Simple Probability

1. PINS AND NEEDLES A pin is dropped at random onto the rectangle below. The pin lands in one of the small squares. What is the probability that the pin lands inside a gray square?

2. VIDEO GAMES Tyler has 14 video games. Five are action/adventure games, 2 are arcade games, 1 is a racing game, and 6 are sports games. Tyler cannot decide which game to play, so he will choose one without looking. What is the probability that the game he chooses is an arcade game?

3. VOLUNTEERING Aisha surveyed her classmates to find out where they get their news. Of a group of 320 teens, about how many get their news online?

Where Teens Get Their News

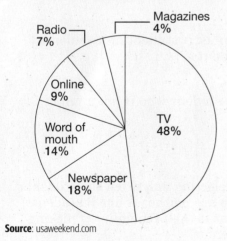

Source: usaweekend.com

4. CANDY A bag of chewy candies contains 22 cherry, 16 green apple, 15 lemonade, 15 orange, and 9 grape candies. Lashanda picks a piece from the bag without looking. What is the probability that she will pick a grape candy? Express the answer as a decimal rounded to the nearest hundredth and as a percent.

FUND-RAISING For Exercises 5–7, use the following information.
To raise money, Angie's class sold 80 boxes of cookies. She made the table below to show which cookies they sold the most.

Bestselling Baker Cookies	
Mints Cookies	25%
Caramel Cookies	19%
Peanut Butter Cookies	13%
Chocolate Cookies	11%
Butter Cookies	9%

5. About how many people bought chocolate cookies?

6. About how many people bought caramel cookies?

7. How many people would you expect to say that they bought another type of Baker Cookie that is not listed in the table?

Lesson 12-7

12-7 Enrichment

Probability and Tables

SCHOOL   In Rockville High School there are

400 freshmen—60 have A averages and 90 have B averages.

300 sophomores—40 have A averages and 60 have B averages.

200 juniors—10 have A averages and 30 have B averages.

100 seniors—20 have A averages and 60 have B averages.

1. Use the information above to complete the table below. Then use the table to answer Exercises 2–11.

Class \ Grade	A	B	Below B	Total
Freshmen				
Sophomores				
Juniors				
Seniors				
Total				

Suppose a student is selected at random from Rockville High School. Find the probability of selecting each of the following.

2. a freshman

3. a senior

4. an A student

5. a student whose grade is below B

6. a sophomore B student

7. a junior A student or a senior A student

8. a student who is neither a junior A student nor a senior A student

9. a B student who is *not* a junior

10. If selecting only from the juniors, what is the probability of picking an A student?

11. If selecting only from the students who are neither A nor B students, what is the probability of picking a senior?

12-8 Lesson Reading Guide

Counting Outcomes

Get Ready for the Lesson

Read the introduction to Lesson 12-8 in your textbook. Write your answers below.

a. Write the names of each deck choice on 5 sticky notes of one color. Write the names of each type of wheel on 3 notes of another color.

b. Choose one deck note and one wheel note. One possible skateboard is Alien, Eagle.

c. Make a list of all the possible skateboards.

d. How many different skateboard designs are possible?

Read the Lesson

Write a definition and give an example of each new vocabulary phrase.

Vocabulary	Definition	Example
1. tree diagram		
2. Fundamental Counting Principle		

Remember What You Learned

3. Complete the two diagrams below by filling in each blank with one of the following words. Some words may be used more than once.

choices

favorable

outcomes

possible

Fundamental Counting Principle	$m \dfrac{}{\text{for event 1}} \times n \dfrac{}{\text{for event 2}} = \dfrac{\text{number of}}{}$
Probability	Probability $= \dfrac{\text{number of} \underline{}}{\text{number of} \underline{}}$

12-8 Study Guide and Intervention

Counting Outcomes

Example 1 How many different combinations of beverage and bread can be made from 3 beverage choices and 3 bread choices?

Draw a **tree diagram** to find the number of different combinations.

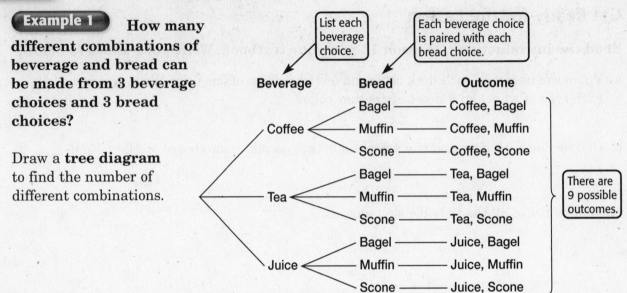

The **Fundamental Counting Principle** also relates the number of outcomes to the number of choices. When you know the number of outcomes, you can find the probability that an event will occur.

Example 2 Refer to Example 1. What is the probability of randomly selecting coffee with a scone?

Use the Fundamental Counting Principle to find the number of outcomes.

Only one of the 9 possible outcomes is coffee and a scone.
So, the probability of randomly selecting coffee with a scone is $\frac{1}{9}$.

Exercises

Find the number of possible outcomes for each situation.

1. one six-sided number cube is rolled, and one card is drawn from a 52-card deck

2. There are 512 juniors and 498 seniors. One junior and one senior are randomly drawn as raffle winners.

Find the probability of each event.

3. A coin is tossed and a card is drawn from a 52-card deck. What is the probability of getting tails and the ten of diamonds?

4. Four coins are tossed. What is the probability of four tails?

12-8 Skills Practice

Counting Outcomes

Draw a tree diagram to find the number of outcomes for each situation.

1. Three coins are tossed.

2. A number cube is rolled and a coin is tossed.

Find the number of possible outcomes for each situation.

3. One card is drawn from a standard deck of cards.

4. Three six-sided number cubes are rolled.

5. One coin is flipped three consecutive times.

6. One coin is flipped and one eight-sided die is rolled.

7. A sweater comes in 3 sizes and 6 colors.

8. A restaurant offers dinners with a choice each of two salads, six entrees, and five desserts.

Find the probability of each event.

9. Draw the ace of spades from a standard deck of cards.

10. A coin is tossed twice. What is the probability of getting two tails?

11. Draw the six of clubs from a standard deck of cards.

12. Roll a 4 or higher on a six-sided number cube.

13. Roll a 7 or an 8 on an eight-sided die.

14. Roll an even number on an eight-sided die.

15. Draw a club from a standard deck of cards.

16. Roll an odd number on a six-sided number cube.

17. A coin is tossed and an eight-sided die is rolled. What is the probability that the coin lands on tails, and the die lands on a 2?

18. A coin is tossed and a card is drawn from a standard deck of cards. What is the probability of landing on tails and choosing a red card?

Lesson 12-8

12-8 Practice

Counting Outcomes

Find the number of possible outcomes for each situation.

1. Joan randomly dials a seven-digit phone number.

2. First-year students at a school must choose one each of 5 English classes, 4 history classes, 5 math classes, and 3 physical education classes.

3. One card each is drawn from four different standard decks of cards.

4. A store offers running shoes with either extra stability or extra cushioning from four different manufacturers.

5. A winter sweater comes in wool or fleece, with a zipper or a crew neck, and in three colors.

6. One spinner can land on red, green, blue, or yellow and another can land on right foot, left foot, right hand, or left hand. Each spinner is spun once.

Find the probability of each event.

7. A number cube is rolled. What is the probability of rolling a 4 or lower?

8. A number cube is rolled. What is the probability of getting a five or higher?

9. An eight-sided die is rolled and a coin is tossed. What is the probability of landing on an even number and getting heads?

10. A coin is tossed and a card is drawn from a standard deck of cards. What is the probability of landing on heads and choosing a heart?

11. **REFRESHMENTS** How many fruit smoothies are possible from 6 choices of fruit, 4 choices of milk, and 3 sizes?

12. **MONOGRAMS** A school's class rings can include a student's initials in an engraved monogram on the ring. How many different monograms are possible from 2 sizes, 5 type styles, and 3 border styles?

13. **MOBILE PHONES** The table shows the features you can choose for a pay-as-you go phone plan.

    a. How many phone plans have national long distance?

    b. How many customized phone plans include 100 minutes per month talkingtime and paging capabilities?

Phone	Features	Calling Area	Monthly Talk Time
Brand A; Brand B	e-mail only; paging only; deluxe: paging and e-mail	local only; local and regional; national long distance	30 min; 60 min; 100 min

12-8 Word Problem Practice
Counting Outcomes

1. **SPORTS** Khalil plays on the interleague soccer team at school. The team has practice jerseys for the players. The jerseys come in blue, black, or gray, in sizes small, medium, and large. Draw a tree diagram to list all of the practice jerseys Khalil can choose from.

2. **CLOTHING** Brittany is choosing an outfit to wear to the football game on Friday night. She has 5 sweaters, 7 turtlenecks, and 8 pairs of pants from which to choose. How many different outfits can she choose from?

3. **GAMES** Jen and Travis are playing a game that requires each player to roll a number cube and choose one ball from a bag without looking that contains one red, one blue, one green, and two yellow balls. The player that rolls an even number and chooses a yellow ball is the winner. What is the probability of a player rolling an even number and drawing a yellow ball without looking?

4. **FOOD** A local bookstore offers a limited sandwich menu for their lunch-time customers. The choices are listed in the table below. How many different kinds of sandwiches does the bookstore offer?

Bread	Meat	Condiments
White	Turkey	Lettuce
Wheat	Roast Beef	Tomato
Rye	Ham	Cheese
Italian		Onions

LICENSE PLATES For Exercises 5–8, use the following information.
Chet noticed that most of the license plate numbers in his state have three letters, A through Z, followed by three digits, 0 through 9.

5. How many different three-letter combinations are there for a license plate?

6. How many different three-digit combinations are there for a license plate?

7. How many different license plates can the state issue?

8. The license plate on Chet's mother's car is CPD 290, which are Chet's initials. What is the probability of his mother getting that license plate?

Lesson 12-8

12-8 Enrichment

Outcomes

Complete.

1. Complete the spinner so that it will have six different possible outcomes.

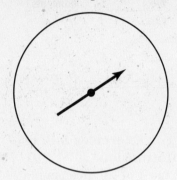

2. List the numbers that could be placed on the die to provide only four different possible outcomes.

3. Complete the spinner so that it is more likely to land on red than blue.

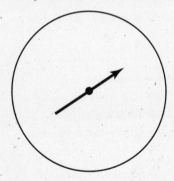

4. List the months in which you could choose a date and have 30 possible outcomes.

5. There are white, green, and blue marbles in a bag. What is the minimum number of each so that it is twice as likely that you draw a green one as a white one, and three times as likely that you draw a blue one as a green one?

6. A year between 1950 and 2001 is chosen at random. How many possible outcomes are there where the year is a leap year? List them.

12-9 Lesson Reading Guide

Permutations and Combinations

Get Ready for the Lesson

Read the introduction to Lesson 12-9 in your textbook. Write your answers below.

a. Make a list of all possible pairs for class offices. (*Note:* Lenora-Michael is different than Michael-Lenora.)

b. How does the Fundamental Counting Principle relate to the number of pairs you found?

c. Make another list for student council seats. (*Note:* For this list, Lenora-Michael is the same as Michael-Lenora.)

d. How does the answer in part **a** compare to the answer in part **c**?

Read the Lesson

Write a definition and give an example of each new vocabulary word.

Vocabulary	Definition	Example
1. permutation		
2. factorial		
3. combination		

Remember What You Learned

4. Complete the diagram at right by writing the words *combinations* and *permutations* in the correct blanks. Then write a sentence based on the diagram stating how to remember the difference between permutations and combinations.

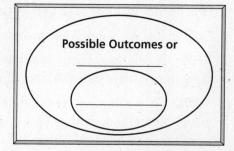

Possible Outcomes or
_____
_____

Lesson 12-9

12-9 Study Guide and Intervention

Permutations and Combinations

<table>
<tr><td rowspan="3">Permutations</td><td>Words</td><td>An arrangement or listing in which order is important is called a permutation.</td></tr>
<tr><td>Symbols</td><td>$P(m, n)$ means m number of choices taken n at a time.</td></tr>
<tr><td>Example</td><td>$P(3, 2) = 3 \cdot 2 = 6$</td></tr>
<tr><td rowspan="3">Combinations</td><td>Words</td><td>An arrangement or listing where order is not important is called a combination.</td></tr>
<tr><td>Symbols</td><td>$C(m, n) = \dfrac{P(m, n)}{n!}$</td></tr>
<tr><td>Example</td><td>$C(6, 2) = \dfrac{P(6, 2)}{2!} = \dfrac{6 \cdot 5}{2 \cdot 1}$ or 15</td></tr>
</table>

Example 1 SPORTS **How many ways can the top five finishers be arranged in a 20-person cross-country race?**

Order is important.
So, this arrangement is a permutation.

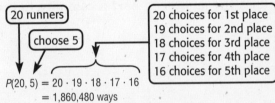

$P(20, 5) = 20 \cdot 19 \cdot 18 \cdot 17 \cdot 16$
$= 1,860,480$ ways

Example 2 SCHOOL **In a science class with 42 students, how many 3-person lab teams can be formed?**

Order is not important.
So, this arrangement is a combination.

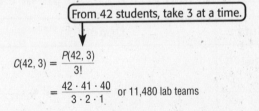

$C(42, 3) = \dfrac{P(42, 3)}{3!}$

$= \dfrac{42 \cdot 41 \cdot 40}{3 \cdot 2 \cdot 1}$ or 11,480 lab teams

Exercises

Tell whether each situation is a *permutation* or *combination*. Then solve.

1. How many ways can three people be selected from a group of seven?

2. How many ways can a 6-person kickball team be chosen from 27 students?

3. How many ways can 15 actors fill 6 roles in a play?

4. How many ways can 5 books be borrowed from a collection of 40 books?

5. JOBS A telemarketing firm has 35 applicants for 8 identical entry-level positions. How many ways can the firm choose 8 employees?

6. FOOD A pizza place sends neighbors a coupon for a 4 topping pizza of any size. If the pizzeria has 15 toppings and 3 sizes to choose from, how many possible pizzas could be purchased using the coupon?

12-9 Skills Practice

Permutations and Combinations

Tell whether each situation is a *permutation* or *combination*. Then solve.

1. How many ways can 6 student desks be arranged in a row?

2. How many ways can 18 baseball cards be passed out to 2 students?

3. How many ways can 10 students line up for lunch?

4. How many ways can you choose 4 CDs from a stack of 8 CDs?

5. How many ways can 3 pairs of shoes be chosen from 8 pairs?

6. How many ways can 9 runners be arranged on a 4-person relay team?

Find each value.

7. 9!   8. 5!   9. 3!

10. 4!   11. 6!   12. 12!

13. **SPORTS**   The Eastern Division of a baseball league is composed of 5 teams. How many different ways can teams of the Eastern Division finish?

14. **LEISURE**   The local hobby store has 17 model airplanes to display. If the front case holds 6 models, how many ways can 6 planes be chosen for the front of the store?

15. **ZOOS**   The local zoo has 23 animals it can take on visits to schools and other community centers. How many ways can the zoo directors choose 9 animals for a trip to a middle school?

16. **CULTURE**   There are 15 Irish dancers in a championship-level competition. How many ways can the top 3 finishers be arranged?

17. **RACING**   In an auto race, the cars start in 11 rows of 3. How many ways can the front row be made from the field of 33 race cars?

TELEVISION   For Exercises 18 and 19, use the following information.
A television network has a choice of 11 new shows for 4 consecutive time slots.

18. How many ways can four shows be chosen, without considering the age of the viewers or the popularity of the time slots?

19. How many ways can the shows be arranged if the time slots are during prime time and in competition for viewers?

Lesson 12-9

12-9 Practice

Permutations and Combinations

Tell whether each situation is a *permutation* or *combination*. Then solve.

1. How many ways can you make a sandwich by choosing 4 of 10 ingredients?

2. How many ways can 11 photographs be arranged horizontally?

3. How many ways can you buy 2 software titles from a choice of 12?

4. How many ways can a baseball manager make a 9-player batting order from a group of 16 players?

5. How many ways can 30 students be arranged in a 4-student line?

6. How many ways can 3 cookie batches be chosen out of 6 prize-winning batches?

7. **SCHOOL TRIPS** Students are chosen in groups of 6 to tour a local business. How many ways can 6 students be selected from 3 classes totaling 53 students?

8. **CONTESTS** In a raffle, 5 winners get to choose from 5 prizes, starting with the first name drawn. If 87 people entered the raffle, how many ways can the winners be arranged?

9. **RESTAURANTS** A local restaurant specializes in simple and tasty meals.

   a. How many sandwiches are possible if the restaurant lets you build a sandwich by choosing any 4 of 10 sandwich ingredients?

   b. If there are 6 soups to choose from, how many soup-and build-a-sandwich specials are possible?

10. **SPORTS** An inline skate has 4 wheels. How many ways could 4 replacement wheels be chosen from a pack of 10 wheels and fitted to a skate?

GIFT WRAPPING For Exercises 11–14, use the following information.

An upscale department offers its customers free gift wrapping on any day that they spend at least $100. The store offers 5 box sizes (XS, S, M, L, XL), 6 wrapping themes (birthday, wedding, baby girl, baby boy, anniversary, and all-occasion), and 3 styles of bow (classic, modern, and jazzy).

11. How many ways can packages be gift-wrapped at the store?

12. What is the probability that any wrapped package will be in a large box?

13. What is the probability that any wrapped package will *not* have a jazzy bow?

14. What is the probability that a customer will request wrapping for a baby-boy gift?

12-9 Word Problem Practice

Permutations and Combinations

1. SOFTBALL There are 10 players on Julia's softball team. The coach is deciding on the batting order for the next game. How many different orders does the coach have to choose the first 4 batters?

2. PIZZA The owner of the Pizza Village wants to advertise her pizza shop on the radio. The table below shows all of the different pizzas the Pizza Village offers. How many different 1-topping pizzas can she say they offer?

Pizza Village		
Crust	**Size**	**Toppings**
Thin	Small	Extra cheese
Thick	Medium	Sausage
Deep-dish	Large	Mushrooms
		Olives
		Onions
		Vegetables
		Pepperoni
		Sausage

3. FOOTBALL Ryan and Gus play on a 6-man football team. The team has 9 players in all. How many different combination of players can their coach put on the field at any one time?

4. LICENSE PLATES In Ohio, license plates are issued with three letters followed by four numbers. The first number cannot be zero. Numbers repeat, but letters do not. How many license plates can Ohio generate with this format?

SOCIAL SECURITY NUMBERS For Exercises 5 and 6, use the following information.
In the United States, each citizen is assigned a nine-digit social security number. The first three digits of the social security number are assigned based on the ZIP code in the mailing address provided on the original application form. The two middle digits of the social security number, which range from 01 through 99, are used to break all of the social security numbers within the same area number into smaller blocks. The last four digits in a social security number run consecutively from 0001 through 9999.

5. How many social security numbers that start with 467 are possible?

6. There are 38 social security area numbers assigned to Texas. How many different social security numbers are possible?

7. There are 72 areas among the 50 states and the District of Columbia. How many different social security numbers are possible?

Lesson 12-9

12-9 Enrichment

Permutations and Combinations

An arrangement of objects *in a given order* is called a **permutation** of the objects. A symbol for the number of permutations is $P(n, x)$, where x represents the number of objects to be arranged in order and n reminds us that these objects are chosen from an original set of n objects.

$$P(n, x) = \frac{n!}{(n - x)!}$$

Example 1   If gold, silver, and bronze medals are to be awarded to the first 3 finishers in an 8-person race, in how many ways can the medals be awarded?

$P(8, 3) = \frac{8!}{5!}$

$\quad = \frac{8 \cdot 7 \cdot 6 \cdot 5 \cdot 4 \cdot 3 \cdot 2 \cdot 1}{5 \cdot 4 \cdot 3 \cdot 2 \cdot 1}$

$\quad = 8 \cdot 7 \cdot 6$

$\quad = 336$ ways in which the medals may be awarded

A selection of x objects taken from a set of n objects *without regard for order* of the selection is called a **combination**. A symbol for the number of combinations is $C(n, x)$.

$$C(n, x) = \frac{n!}{x!(n - x)!}$$

Example 2   In how many ways can you choose 3 people from a group of 12 without regard for order?

$C(12, 3) = \frac{12!}{3!9!}$

$\quad = \frac{12 \cdot 11 \cdot 10 \cdot 9 \cdot 8 \cdot 7 \cdot 6 \cdot 5 \cdot 4 \cdot 3 \cdot 2 \cdot 1}{(3 \cdot 2 \cdot 1)(9 \cdot 8 \cdot 7 \cdot 6 \cdot 5 \cdot 4 \cdot 3 \cdot 2 \cdot 1)}$

$\quad = \frac{12 \cdot 11 \cdot 10}{3 \cdot 2}$

$\quad = 220$ possible groups of 3 people

Find each value.

1. $P(7, 2)$

2. $P(7, 5)$

3. $C(7, 2)$

4. $C(7, 5)$

5. $P(13, 2)$

6. $C(13, 11)$

12-10 **Lesson Reading Guide**

Probability of Composite Events

Get Ready for the Lesson

Read the introduction to Lesson 12-10 in your textbook. Write your answers below.

a. What was your experimental probability for the red then white outcome?

b. Would you expect the probability to be different if you did not place the first counter back in the bag? Explain your reasoning.

Read the Lesson

Write a definition and give an example of each new vocabulary phrase.

Vocabulary	Definition	Example
1. composite events		
2. independent events		
3. dependent events		
4. mutually exclusive events		

You are finding the probability of choosing the following arrangements of counters from a bag containing red, orange, and blue counters. Label each situation with independent events, dependent events, or mutually exclusive events.

5. a red counter, which is replaced, followed by a blue counter _____

6. an orange counter or a primary color _____

7. an orange counter, which is kept out of the bag, followed by a red counter

_____

Remember What You Learned

8. Complete the concept map below with the vocabulary phrases from this lesson.

One event, then the other
P(A AND B)

Probability of Two Events

Does the outcome of the first event influence the outcome of the second event?

yes ☐_____

no ☐_____

One event, or the other
P(A OR B)

☐_____

Lesson 12-10

12-10 Study Guide and Intervention

Probability of Composite Events

Probability of Two Independent Events	Words	The probability of two independent events is found by multiplying the probability of the first event by the probability of the second event.
	Symbols	$P(A \text{ and } B) = P(A) \cdot P(B)$
Probability of Two Dependent Events	Words	If two events, A and B, are dependent, then the probability of events occurring is the product of the probability of A and the probability of B after A occurs.
	Symbols	$P(A \text{ and } B) = P(A) \cdot P(B \text{ following } A)$

Example 1   **GAMES**   A card is drawn from a standard deck of 52 cards. The card is replaced and another is drawn. Find the probability if the first card is the 3 of hearts and the second card is the 2 of clubs.

Since the first card is replaced, the events are independent.

$P(3 \text{ of hearts and 2 of clubs}) = P(3 \text{ of hearts}) \cdot P(2 \text{ of clubs})$

$= \dfrac{1}{52} \cdot \dfrac{1}{52}$

$= \dfrac{1}{2704}$

The probability is $\dfrac{1}{2704}$.

Probability of Mutually Exclusive Events	Words	The probability of one or the other of two **mutually exclusive events** can be found by adding the probability of the first event to the probability of the second event.
	Symbols	$P(A \text{ or } B) = P(A) + P(B)$

Example 2   The spinner at the right is spun. What is the probability that the spinner will stop on 7 or an even number?

The events are mutually exclusive because the spinner cannot stop on both 7 and an even number at the same time.

$P(7 \text{ or even}) = P(7) + P(\text{even}) = \dfrac{1}{8} + \dfrac{1}{2} = \dfrac{5}{8}$

The probability that the spinner will stop on 7 or an even number is $\dfrac{5}{8}$.

Exercises

A card is drawn from a standard deck of cards. The card is not replaced and a second card is drawn. Find each probability.

1. $P(4 \text{ and } 8)$

2. $P(\text{queen of hearts and } 10)$

A card is drawn from a standard deck of cards. Find each probability.

3. $P(\text{queen of clubs or a red card})$

4. $P(\text{queen of hearts or } 10)$

12-10 Skills Practice

Probability of Composite Events

A number cube is rolled and the spinner is spun. Find each probability.

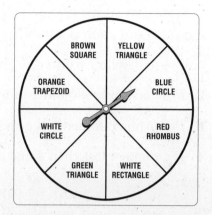

1. P(2 and green triangle)

2. P(an odd number and a circle)

3. P(a prime number and a quadrilateral)

4. P(a number greater than 4 and a parallelogram)

There are 5 yellow marbles, 1 purple marble, 3 green marbles, and 3 red marbles in a bag. Once a marble is drawn, it is replaced. Find the probability of each outcome.

5. a purple then a red marble

6. a red then a green marble

7. two green marbles in a row

8. two red marbles in a row

9. a purple then a green marble

10. a red then a yellow marble

There are 4 yellow marbles, 3 purple marbles, 1 green marble, and 1 white marble in a bag. Once a marble is drawn, it is *not* replaced. Find the probability of each outcome.

11. a purple then a white marble

12. a white then a green marble

13. two purple marbles in a row

14. two yellow marbles in a row

15. a yellow then a purple marble

16. a green then a white marble

A card is drawn from a standard deck of cards. Find the probability of each outcome.

17. P(a red card or a club)

18. P(a diamond or a spade)

19. P(a face card or a 2)

20. P(a 7 or a 9)

21. P(a red card or a king of spades)

22. P(a heart or a queen of diamonds)

Lesson 12-10

12-10 Practice

Probability of Composite Events

An eight-sided die is rolled and the spinner is spun. Find each probability.

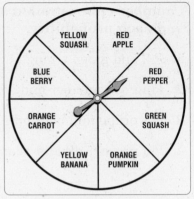

1. P(4 and yellow fruit or vegetable)

2. P(an odd number and a pumpkin)

3. P(a prime number and a red fruit or vegetable)

4. P(a number less than 4 and a blue fruit or vegetable)

There are 6 orange marbles, 2 red marbles, 3 white marbles, and 4 green marbles in a bag. Once a marble is drawn, it is replaced. Find the probability of each outcome.

5. a red then a white marble

6. a white then a green marble

7. two orange marbles in a row

8. two marbles in a row that are *not* white

9. a green then a *not* green marble

10. a red then an orange then a green marble

There are 2 green marbles, 7 blue marbles, 3 white marbles, and 4 purple marbles in a bag. Once a marble is drawn, it is *not* replaced. Find the probability of each outcome.

11. a green then a white marble

12. a blue then a purple marble

13. two blue marbles in a row

14. two marbles in a row that are *not* purple

15. a white then a purple marble

16. three purple marbles in a row

The chart shows the letter-number combinations for bingo. The balls are randomly drawn one at a time. Balls are *not* replaced after they are drawn. Find the probability of each outcome.

B	I	N	G	O
1	13	25	37	49
2	14	26	38	50
3	15	27	39	51
4	16	28	40	52
5	17	29	41	53
6	18	30	42	54
7	19	31	43	55
8	20	32	44	56
9	21	33	45	57
10	22	34	46	58
11	23	35	47	59
12	24	36	48	60

17. a B-1

18. a G

19. an N or a B-2

20. an I or an O

21. *not* a G

22. a B-6, then a G, then

another G

12-10 Word Problem Practice

Probability of Composite Events

1. **BIRTHDAYS** Sarah's birthday and Dakota's birthday are both in May. What is the probability that their birthdays are the same day in May?

2. **GAMES** Marvin and Greg are playing a card game. The deck of cards has 25 red cards, 25 yellow cards, 25 blue cards, 25 green cards, and 8 wild cards. Marvin shuffles the deck two times before he starts to deal the cards. What is the probability that the first card Marvin deals is yellow or wild card?

3. **DOMINOES** A set of dominoes contains 91 tiles, with the numbers on the tiles ranging from 0 to 12. There are 13 tiles that have the same number on each end. These tiles are called doubles. To begin a game, each player draws one tile, which is not returned to the pile. What is the probability that the first and second players each draw a double?

4. **MONEY** Mr. Santiago pulls two bills at random from the 4 $1 bills, 3 $5 bills, and 1 $20 bill in his pocket. What is the probability that he chooses one $1 bill and one $5 bill?

ANALYZE GRAPHS For Excercises 5 and 6, use the information below.

The graph shows the favorite sports team of teens between the ages of 15 and 18.

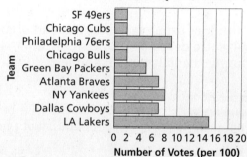

Favorite Sports Team

Source: www.stamats.com/stamatsstats/stamatstatvol2no11.htm

5. What is the probability that one teen likes the Dallas Cowboys and another likes the Atlanta Braves? Express as a percent rounded to the nearest tenth.

6. What is the probability that one teen likes the L.A. Lakers and another likes the N.Y. Yankees? Express as a percent rounded to the nearest thousandth.

Lesson 12-10

12-10 Enrichment

Probability of Dependent Events

Look at the letters in the word MATHEMATICAL. If these letters were placed in a hat, what would be the probability of drawing a vowel and then, without replacing the vowel, drawing a consonant? These are **dependent events** since the letter selected on the first draw affects the probability for the second draw.

$$P(\text{vowel, then consonant}) = \frac{5}{12} \cdot \frac{7}{11} = \frac{35}{132}$$

Find the probability of drawing each of the following from the letters in MATHEMATICAL if the letters are not replaced.

1. two Ms

2. two As

3. three As

4. three vowels

5. five consonants

6. the letters MATH in that order

Now, think of using variables instead of numbers. This is very useful, since this is the way formulas are developed. Once a formula is found, it can be used for any numbers. Begin by examining the following example.

Example Three of 10 socks in a box are blue. If socks are drawn without looking and not replaced, what is the probability of picking 3 blue socks in 3 drawings?

$$\frac{3}{10} \cdot \frac{2}{9} \cdot \frac{1}{8} = \frac{6}{720}, \text{ or } \frac{1}{120}$$

7. If box containing n socks has k blue ones, what is the probability of picking 3 blue socks in 3 drawings?

8. If a box containing n socks has k blue ones, what is the probability of picking x blue socks in x drawings?

9. Use your formula from Exercise 7 to find the probability of picking 3 blue socks in 3 drawings from a box containing 6 socks, 4 of them blue.

10. Use your formula from Exercise 8 to find the probability of picking 4 blue socks in 4 drawings from a box containing 6 socks, 5 of them blue.

12-10 Spreadsheet Activity
Simulating a Composite Probability

Acting out a probability situation is called a **simulation**. You can use a spreadsheet to simulate compound events and investigate compound probability.

Example   **A typical mare can give birth once a year. What is the probability that Rebeca's mare will bear female foals in two consecutive years?**

Step 1 Use the random number generator of the spreadsheet to simulate the events. The formula RANDBETWEEN(0,1) will give a random number between 0 and 1. Let 0 represent a male foal and 1 represent a female foal.

Column A represents the first foal and Column B represents the second. Since 1 represents a female and 0 represents a male,
Column C is the sum of Columns A and B, the number of female foals.

Composite Probability.xls

	A First Foal	B Second Foal	C Number of Females
1			
2	0	1	1
3	1	0	1
4	1	1	2
5	1	1	2
6	0	0	0
7	0	1	1
8	1	1	2
9	1	0	1
10	0	0	0
11	1	0	1

Sheet 1 / Sheet 2 / Sheet 3

Step 2 Use the spreadsheet to conduct 10 trials. Record the number of times that there are 2 females.

Exercises

1. Use the formula $P(A \text{ and } B) = P(A) \cdot P(B)$ to find the probability that Rebeca's mare will bear female foals in two consecutive years.

2. Based on your simulation, in what fraction of the 10 trials are there 2 females? How does this compare to the probability that you found in Exercise 1?

3. Expand your simulation to 100 trials by clicking on the cells in the bottom row and dragging downward. In what fraction of the 100 trials are there 2 females? How does this compare to the fractions that you found in Exercises 1 and 2?

4. What is the probability that Rebeca's mare will bear female foals in three consecutive years? Use the spreadsheet to simulate three foals. In what fraction of the trials are there 3 females? How does this compare to the probability?

Lesson 12-10

12 Student Recording Sheet

Use this recording sheet with pages 696–697 of the Student Edition.

Read each question. Then fill in the correct answer.

1. Ⓐ Ⓑ Ⓒ Ⓓ

2. Ⓕ Ⓖ Ⓗ Ⓘ

3. Record your answer and fill in the bubbles in the grid below. Be sure to use the correct place value.

⓪	⓪	⓪	⓪		⓪	⓪
①	①	①	①		①	①
②	②	②	②		②	②
③	③	③	③		③	③
④	④	④	④		④	④
⑤	⑤	⑤	⑤		⑤	⑤
⑥	⑥	⑥	⑥		⑥	⑥
⑦	⑦	⑦	⑦		⑦	⑦
⑧	⑧	⑧	⑧		⑧	⑧
⑨	⑨	⑨	⑨		⑨	⑨

4. Ⓐ Ⓑ Ⓒ Ⓓ

5. Ⓕ Ⓖ Ⓗ Ⓘ

6. Record your answer and fill in the bubbles in the grid below. Be sure to use the correct place value.

⓪	⓪	⓪	⓪		⓪	⓪
①	①	①	①		①	①
②	②	②	②		②	②
③	③	③	③		③	③
④	④	④	④		④	④
⑤	⑤	⑤	⑤		⑤	⑤
⑥	⑥	⑥	⑥		⑥	⑥
⑦	⑦	⑦	⑦		⑦	⑦
⑧	⑧	⑧	⑧		⑧	⑧
⑨	⑨	⑨	⑨		⑨	⑨

7. Ⓐ Ⓑ Ⓒ Ⓓ

8. Ⓕ Ⓖ Ⓗ Ⓘ

9. Ⓐ Ⓑ Ⓒ Ⓓ

10. Ⓕ Ⓖ Ⓗ Ⓘ

11. Ⓐ Ⓑ Ⓒ Ⓓ

12. Ⓕ Ⓖ Ⓗ Ⓘ

13. Ⓐ Ⓑ Ⓒ Ⓓ

Pre-AP

Record your answers for Question 14 on the back of this paper.

12 Rubric for Scoring Pre-AP

(Use to score the Pre-AP question on page 697 of the Student Edition.)

General Scoring Guidelines

- If a student gives only a correct numerical answer to a problem but does not show how he or she arrived at the answer, the student will be awarded only 1 credit. All extended response questions require the student to show work.

- A fully correct answer for a multiple-part question requires correct responses for all parts of the question. For example, if a question has three parts, the correct response to one or two parts of the question that required work to be shown is *not* considered a fully correct response.

- Students who use trial and error to solve a problem must show their method. Merely showing that the answer checks or is correct is not considered a complete response for full credit.

Exercise 14 Rubric

Score	Specific Criteria
4	A correct solution that is supported by well-developed, accurate explanations. 80–89 is the interval with the greatest number of test scores. $\left(\dfrac{9}{12}\right)$75% of the class scored between 70 and 89. The histogram is complete with labels.
3	A generally correct solution, but may contain minor flaws in reasoning or computation.
2	A partially correct interpretation and/or solution to the problem.
1	A correct solution with no supporting evidence or explanation.
0	An incorrect solution indicating no mathematical understanding of the concept or task, or no solution is given.

12   Chapter 12 Quiz 1

(Lessons 12–1 through 12–3)

BASEBALL Use the table at the right.

1. Display the data set in a stem-and-leaf plot.

2. In which interval do most of the players fall?

Given the set of data 45, 62, 72, 51, 68, 47, 69, 50, 75, find the following.

3. the median

4. the upper and lower quartiles

5. Draw a box-and-whisker plot for the set of data and find the interquartile range.

Home Runs Scored by Major League Leaders in 2001	
Bonds	73
Gonzalez	57
Green	49
Helton	49
Palmeiro	47
Rodriguez	52
Sexson	45
Sosa	64
Thome	49

Source: www.mlb.com

1. _____

2. _____

3. _____

4. _____

5. 40 45 50 55 60 65 70 75

_____

- -

12   Chapter 12 Quiz 2

(Lessons 12–4 and 12–5)

VIDEOS For Questions 1–4, use the frequency table shown.

1. Display the data in a histogram.

Video Games Purchased in the Last 12 Months		
Video Games	Tally	Frequency
1–3	ЖЖЖЖ III	18
4–6	ЖЖ I	11
7–9	ЖЖ II	7
10–12	II	2
13–15	I	1

1.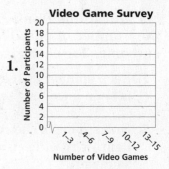

2. How many people were surveyed?

3. How many people surveyed bought at least 7 video games?

Select an appropriate type of display for each set of data.

4. percent of students who voted for the homecoming queen in each homeroom

5. the relationship among people who have at least 1 dog, at least 1 cat, have both, or neither

2. _____

3. _____

4. _____

5. _____

Assessment

12 Chapter 12 Quiz 3

SCORE _____

(Lessons 12–6 and 12–7)

1. Suppose some of the columns in a histogram are wider than others. How could this affect the impression of the data presented in the histogram?

1. _____

2. Explain why the graphs look different.

2. _____

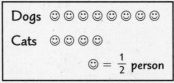

Graph 1	**Graph 2**
Dogs ☺☺	Dogs ☺☺☺☺☺☺☺
Cats ☺	Cats ☺☺☺☺
☺ = 2 people	☺ = $\frac{1}{2}$ person

3. Which graph appears to show that a lot more people prefer dogs to cats as pets? Explain.

3. _____

4. Find the probability of rolling a 5 on a 6-sided number cube.

4. _____

5. Find the probability of rolling an even number on a 6-sided number cube.

5. _____

---

12 Chapter 12 Quiz 4

SCORE _____

(Lessons 12–8 and 12–10)

For Questions 1 and 2, find the number of possible outcomes for each situation.

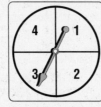

1. Each spinner at the right is spun once.

1. _____

2. Ernesto has a choice between white or wheat bread, turkey, ham, or roast beef, and Swiss or cheddar cheese for his sandwich.

2. _____

3. Find the probability of rolling two threes when two number cubes are rolled.

3. _____

Tell whether the situation in number 4 is a *permutation* or *combination*. Then solve.

4. How many ways can 5 runners place 1st to 5th in a race?

4. _____

5. There are 4 red marbles and 3 blue marbles in a bag. Once a marble is drawn it is *not* replaced. Find the probability of drawing two red marbles in a row.

5. _____

12 Chapter 12 Mid-Chapter Test

SCORE _____

(Lessons 12-1 through 12-5)

Part I *Write the letter for the correct answer in the blank at the right of each question.*

Mrs. O'Neill's class had earned the following first quarter grades in chemistry: 84, 92, 57, 60, 73, 79, 87, 68, 94, 83, 65, 75, 87, 93, 97, 56, and 71.

1. Choose the ordered leaves that would appear on stem "8" in a stem-and-leaf plot of the grades.

   A. 1, 3, 5, 9   **B.** 3, 4, 7, 7   **C.** 9, 5, 3, 1   **D.** 7, 7, 4, 3   1. _____

2. What is the interquartile range of the grades?

   F. 41   **G.** 87   **H.** 23   **J.** 78   2. _____

WEATHER Use the box-and-whisker plot.

High Temperatures, February

3. What fraction of the days in the month had high temperatures less than 15°F?

   A. $\frac{1}{4}$ **B.** $\frac{1}{3}$ **C.** $\frac{1}{2}$ **D.** $\frac{3}{4}$ 3. _____

4. Exactly half of the days had highs over what temperature?

   F. 15°   **G.** 30°   **H.** 35°   **J.** 45°   4. _____

Part II

SCHOOL Use the set of data shown.

5. Display the data in a histogram.

Test Scores		
Score	Tally	Frequency
95–100	IIII	4
89–94	IHT IIII	9
83–88	IHT II	7
77–82	IHT	5
71–76	III	3
65–70	IIII	4

5.
Test Scores

6. How many students scored above 76?   6. _____

Choose an appropriate display for each set of data.

7. average price of a gallon of milk over the past 20 years   7. _____

8. the number of students who chose each subject as their favorite subject   8. _____

Assessment

12 Chapter 12 Vocabulary Test

back-to-back stem-and-leaf plot	Fundamental Counting Principle	measures of variation	stem-and-leaf plot
box-and-whisker plot	histogram	mutually exclusive events	stems
combination	independent events	outliers	tree diagram
compound events	interquartile range	permutation	upper quartile
dependent events	leaves	quartiles	Venn diagram
factorial	lower quartile	range	
		simulations	

Underline or circle the correct term or phrase to complete each sentence.

1. In a (*box-and-whisker plot, histogram, stem-and-leaf plot*), numerical data are listed in ascending or descending order.

2. In a stem-and-leaf plot, the greatest place value of the data forms the (*leaves, outliers, stems*).

3. The (*interquartile range, quartile, range*) is the difference between the median of the lower half of a set of data and the median of the upper half of a set of data.

4. A (*box-and-whisker plot, histogram, stem-and-leaf plot*) divides a set of data into four parts using the median and quartiles.

5. Data that are more than 1.5 times the interquartile range from the quartiles are called (*leaves, odds, outliers*).

6. A (*box-and-whisker plot, histogram, stem-and-leaf plot*) uses bars to display numerical data that have been organized into equal intervals.

7. An arrangement or listing in which order is important is called a (*combination, factorial, permutation*).

8. The (*lower quartile, range*) is a measure of variation that is the difference between the least and greatest values in a set of data.

9. In (*dependent, independent*) events, the outcome of one event does not influence the outcome of a second event.

10. If two events cannot happen at the same time, they are said to be (*dependent events, independent events, mutually exclusive events*).

Define each term in your own words.

11. Fundamental Counting Principle

12. measures of variation

13. back-to-back stem-and-leaf plots

12) Chapter 12 Test, Form 1

Write the letter for the correct answer in the blank at the right of each question.

For Questions 1–3, use the data set {14, 24, 32, 26, 10, 56}.

1. In a stem-and-leaf plot of the data, which number would *not* appear as a leaf?
   A. 0   **B.** 4   **C.** 6   **D.** 3   1. _____

2. What are the stems for the data set?
   F. {0, 2, 4, 6}   **G.** {1, 2, 3, 4, 5}   **H.** {1, 2, 3, 5}   **J.** {0, 1, 2, 3, 5}   2. _____

3. Find the interquartile range of the data.
   A. 15   **B.** 18   **C.** 46   **D.** 25   3. _____

4. Which measure would you use to describe the difference in height of five friends?
   F. lower quartile   **G.** mean   **H.** median   **J.** range   4. _____

For Questions 5 and 6, use the box-and-whisker plot shown.

Points per Game

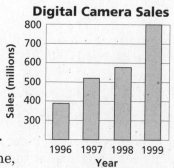

5. What percent of the games had a point total of less than 50?
   A. 25%   **B.** 50%   **C.** 60%   **D.** 75%   5. _____

6. What is the highest number of points scored in one game?
   F. 35   **G.** 50   **H.** 60   **J.** 75   6. _____

7. What is the probability of getting two tails when two coins are tossed?
   A. $\frac{1}{2}$ **B.** $\frac{1}{4}$ **C.** $\frac{1}{16}$ **D.** $\frac{1}{8}$ 7. _____

8. How many ways can 5 students line up to buy lunch?
   F. 6   **G.** 36   **H.** 120   **J.** 720   8. _____

9. Find the value of $P(6, 4)$.
   A. 10   **B.** 24   **C.** 360   **D.** 720   9. _____

10. Which sentence is a true statement about the data in the graph at the right?
    F. Sales doubled from 1996 to 1997.
    G. Sales tripled from 1996 to 1999.
    H. Sales doubled from 1996 to 1999.
    J. Sales tripled from 1996 to 1998.   10. _____

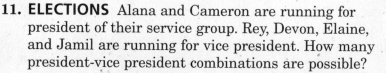

11. **ELECTIONS** Alana and Cameron are running for president of their service group. Rey, Devon, Elaine, and Jamil are running for vice president. How many president-vice president combinations are possible?
    A. 6   **B.** 24   **C.** 12   **D.** 8   11. _____

Digital Camera Sales

Source: www.usatoday.com

Assessment

12   Chapter 12 Test, Form 1   *(continued)*

For Questions 12 and 13, use the histogram shown.

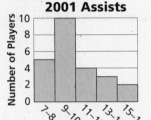

Major League Soccer 2001 Assists

Source: www.mlsnet.com

12. Which of the following is *not* an interval?

   F. 9–10   **H.** 7–8

   G. 4–5   **J.** 15–16

12. _____

13. Which interval has the most players?

   A. 7–8   **C.** 9–10

   B. 13–14   **D.** 11–12

13. _____

14. **YEARBOOK** The yearbook editor has room for 4 pictures on the last page of the yearbook. She has 6 pictures from which to choose. How many combinations of 4 pictures can she choose?

   F. 15   **G.** 10   **H.** 24   **J.** 360

14. _____

15. How many ways can 5 runners come in first, second and third places?

   A. 125   **B.** 15   **C.** 60   **D.** 12

15. _____

16. How many 2 digit numbers can be formed if the first number must be 1 through 9 and the second number can be 0 through 9?

   F. 100   **G.** 19   **H.** 99   **J.** 90

16. _____

17. Two 6-sided dice are rolled. Find the probability for rolling an odd number on one die and a 6 on the other.

   A. $\frac{1}{12}$ **B.** $\frac{1}{2}$ **C.** $\frac{1}{6}$ **D.** $\frac{1}{36}$

17. _____

18. Kevin has nine cards numbered 1 to 9. What is the probability of randomly picking two odd-numbered cards if the first card picked is *not* replaced?

   F. $\frac{4}{9}$ **G.** $\frac{2}{9}$ **H.** $\frac{5}{18}$ **J.** $\frac{1}{2}$

18. _____

19. A box holds 26 cards. On each card is a different letter of the alphabet. What is the probability of randomly choosing either *X* or *Y*?

   A. $\frac{1}{26}$ **B.** $\frac{1}{2}$ **C.** $\frac{1}{13}$ **D.** $\frac{2}{25}$

19. _____

20. An 8-sided die is rolled. What is the probability of rolling a 3 or an even number?

   F. $\frac{5}{8}$ **G.** $\frac{1}{8}$ **H.** $\frac{1}{2}$ **J.** $\frac{1}{4}$

20. _____

Bonus   A bag contains 4 red, 20 blue, and 6 green marbles. Tia and Amy each pick one at random and keep it. What is the probability that they each select a red marble?   **B:** _____

12 **Chapter 12 Test, Form 2A** SCORE _____

Write the letter for the correct answer in the blank at the right of each question.

TEMPERATURE Use the set of data at the right.

High Temperatures for September 9, 2001 (°F)			
Atlanta	86	Miami	88
Chicago	80	Omaha	71
Duluth	62	San Diego	75
Fargo	66	San Francisco	68

Source: Fort Worth Star-Telegram

1. Which number would *not* appear as a stem in a stem-and-leaf plot of the data?
   A. 5   C. 7
   B. 6   D. 8

   1. _____

2. How many of the cities had a temperature of more than 75°F?
   F. 4   G. 5   H. 3   J. 8

   2. _____

3. Find the lower quartile of the temperatures.
   A. 71   B. 67   C. 73   D. 75

   3. _____

4. Which sentence best describes the data?
   F. The temperatures vary by 26°F.   H. The interquartile range is 15°F.
   G. The median temperature is 71°F.   J. The lowest temperature is 66°F.

   4. _____

Use the box-and-whisker plot shown.

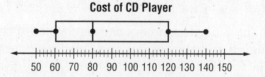

Cost of CD Player

5. Find the interquartile range.
   A. 10   C. 20
   B. 60   D. 40

   5. _____

6. What percent of the CD players cost between $120 and $140?
   F. 75%   G. 30%   H. 50%   J. 25%

   6. _____

For Questions 7 and 8, use the histogram at the right.

7. Which interval has the fewest number of people?
   A. 1–3   C. 7–9
   B. 4–6   D. 10–12

   7. _____

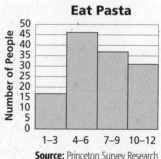

How Often We Eat Pasta

Source: Princeton Survey Research

8. About how many people eat at least 7 servings of pasta each month?
   F. 46   H. 70
   G. 37   J. 120

   8. _____

9. **SALES** Choose the sentence that best describes the data in the graph.
   A. Sales increased 47% from Jan. to Mar.
   B. Sales decreased 47% from Mar. to Apr.
   C. Sales increased 2.5 times from Jan. to Mar.
   D. Sales decreased 2.5 times from Mar. to Apr.

   9. _____

Coffee Bean Sales

10. Flor has seven skirts and seven blouses. How many outfits are possible?

   F. 5040   **G.** 343   **H.** 49   **J.** 14   10. _____

11. An 8-sided die is rolled twice. What is the probability of rolling a 6 and an odd number?

   A. $\frac{3}{64}$ **B.** $\frac{1}{16}$ **C.** $\frac{1}{2}$ **D.** $\frac{1}{8}$ 11. _____

12. How many ways can 7 planes line up on a runway?

   F. 49   **G.** 5040   **H.** 343   **J.** 2401   12. _____

13. **CHORUS** Of 10 altos in the freshman chorus, 5 will sing at a holiday concert. How many groups of 5 altos could be selected from the 10 altos?

   A. 756   **B.** 252   **C.** 378   **D.** 126   13. _____

14. **FAIR** Eight quilts are entered in the county fair. How many ways can the quilts take first, second, and third place?

   F. 512   **G.** 56   **H.** 24   **J.** 336   14. _____

15. How many ways can 10 swimmers come in first, second and third places?

   A. 720   **B.** 1000   **C.** 27   **D.** 3   15. _____

16. How many 3 digit numbers can be formed if the first number must be 1 through 9 and the second and third numbers can be 0 through 9?

   F. 100   **G.** 900   **H.** 99   **J.** 1000   16. _____

17. Two 6-sided dice are rolled. Find the probability of rolling a composite number on one die and a prime on the other.

   A. $\frac{1}{6}$ **B.** $\frac{1}{2}$ **C.** $\frac{1}{3}$ **D.** $\frac{2}{3}$ 17. _____

18. Ella has twelve cards numbered 1 to 12. What is the probability she picks three even-numbered cards in a row, if the first two cards are *not* replaced?

   F. $\frac{1}{11}$ **G.** $\frac{1}{4}$ **H.** $\frac{1}{3}$ **J.** $\frac{1}{8}$ 18. _____

19. A 6-sided die is rolled. What is the probability of rolling a 1, 3, or a 4?

   A. $\frac{1}{3}$ **B.** $\frac{1}{2}$ **C.** $\frac{1}{6}$ **D.** $\frac{2}{3}$ 19. _____

20. A box contains 26 cards. Each card has a different letter of the alphabet on it. What is the probability of randomly picking either A or B?

   F. $\frac{1}{13}$ **G.** $\frac{1}{2}$ **H.** $\frac{1}{26}$ **J.** $\frac{1}{24}$ 20. _____

Bonus Roland usually makes three free throws out of every five attempted. To simulate the probability of Roland making two free throws in a row, Cathy puts 25 marbles in a bag, red for a basket and blue for a miss. After a marble is drawn and recorded, it is replaced. Of the 25 red marbles how many should be red?   **B:** _____

12 Chapter 12 Test, Form 2B

Write the letter for the correct answer in the blank at the right of each question.

TEMPERATURE Use the set of data at the right.

High Temperatures for September 9, 2001 (°F)			
Atlanta	86	Fargo	66
Missoula	60	Miami	88
Chicago	80	Omaha	71
Spokane	70	San Diego	75

Source: *Fort Worth Star-Telegram*

1. Which number would not appear as a leaf in a stem-and-leaf plot of the data?
   A. 5   **C.** 7
   B. 6   **D.** 8

1. _____

2. How many of the cities had a temperature of less than 69°F?
   F. 2   **G.** 4   **H.** 6   **J.** 7

2. _____

3. Find the upper quartile of the temperatures.
   A. 68   **B.** 75   **C.** 83   **D.** 88

3. _____

4. Which sentence best describes the data?
   F. The temperatures vary by 27°F.   **H.** The interquartile range is 16°F.
   G. The median temperature is 73°F.   **J.** The highest temperature is 86°F.

4. _____

Use the box-and-whisker plot shown.

Ages of Museum Employees

5. What percent of employees are between 45 and 70 years old?
   A. 25%   **B.** 50%   **C.** 75%   **D.** 100%

5. _____

6. Find the interquartile range.
   F. 55   **G.** 30   **H.** 25   **J.** 45

6. _____

For Questions 7 and 8, use the histogram at the right.

How Often We Eat Pasta

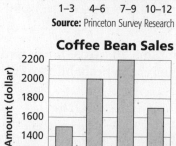

7. Which interval has the greatest number of people?
   A. 1–3   **C.** 7–9
   B. 4–6   **D.** 10–12

7. _____

8. About how many people eat at least 4 servings of pasta each month?
   F. 5   **H.** 70
   G. 45   **J.** 115

8. _____

Source: Princeton Survey Research

9. Choose the sentence that best describes the data in the graph.
   A. Sales doubled from Jan. to Feb.
   B. Sales tripled from Jan. to Mar.
   C. Sales increased 1.3 times from Jan. to Feb.
   D. Sales increased 1.3 times from Jan. to Mar.

9. _____

Coffee Bean Sales

(Assessment)

10. Malik has four pairs of pants and four shirts. How many outfits are possible?
  F. 256   **G.** 16   **H.** 64   **J.** 8   10. _____

11. An 8-sided die is rolled twice. What is the probability of rolling two 3s?
  A. $\frac{1}{8}$ **B.** $\frac{1}{512}$ **C.** $\frac{1}{4}$ **D.** $\frac{1}{64}$ 11. _____

12. How many ways can 8 rings be arranged in a jewelry case display?
  F. 64   **G.** 32,768   **H.** 4096   **J.** 40,320   12. _____

13. **SCHOOL** In English class, each student must read 4 plays from a book of 5 plays. How many different combinations of plays could a student read?
  A. 5   **B.** 20   **C.** 60   **D.** 120   13. _____

14. **FAIR** Seven apple pies are entered in the county fair. How many ways can the pies take first, second, third, and fourth place?
  F. 28   **G.** 840   **H.** 2401   **J.** 35   14. _____

15. How many ways can 11 contestants come in first, second, third and fourth places?
  A. 44   **B.** 1000   **C.** 7920   **D.** 10,000   15. _____

16. How many 3 digit numbers can be formed if the first and second number must be 1 through 9 and the third number can be 0 through 9?
  F. 30   **G.** 27   **H.** 1000   **J.** 810   16. _____

17. Two 6-sided dice are rolled. Find the probability for rolling an odd number on one die and an even number on the other.
  A. $\frac{1}{6}$ **B.** $\frac{1}{2}$ **C.** $\frac{1}{4}$ **D.** $\frac{1}{36}$ 17. _____

18. Ruben has ten cards numbered 1 to 10. What is the probability of picking two even-numbered cards in a row, if the first card picked is *not* replaced?
  F. $\frac{2}{5}$ **G.** $\frac{2}{9}$ **H.** $\frac{1}{5}$ **J.** $\frac{1}{2}$ 18. _____

19. A 6-sided die is rolled. What is the probability of rolling a 4 or a prime number?
  A. $\frac{1}{2}$ **B.** $\frac{1}{3}$ **C.** $\frac{1}{6}$ **D.** $\frac{2}{3}$ 19. _____

20. A box contains 26 cards. Each card has a different letter of the alphabet on it. What is the probability of randomly picking either C, D, or F?
  F. $\frac{1}{13}$ **G.** $\frac{1}{26}$ **H.** $\frac{3}{26}$ **J.** $\frac{1}{24}$ 20. _____

Bonus Produce a list of at least 10 data items that have a median of 25 and an interquartile range of 17.   **B:** _____

12   Chapter 12 Test, Form 2C   SCORE _____

OLYMPICS Use the set of data at the right.

Olympic Medal Tally, Sydney, 2000			
USA	97	France	38
Russia	88	Italy	34
China	59	Netherlands	25
Australia	68	Cuba	29
Germany	57	U.K.	28

Source: www.olympics.indya.com

1. Display the set of data in a stem-and-leaf plot.

    1. _____

2. How many countries won fewer than 60 medals?

    2. _____

3. Find the range and interquartile range for the set of data.

    3. _____

4. How does the lower quartile of the data compare to the least value of the set?

    4. _____

BASEBALL Use the set of data at the right

MLB Strike-out Leaders			
2000	187	1995	150
1999	171	1994	128
1998	171	1993	169
1997	175	1992	154
1996	160	1991	175

Source: www.mlb.com

5. Draw a box-and-whisker plot for the data.

    5.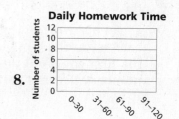
    120 130 140 150 160 170 180 190

6. Find the interquartile range.

    6. _____

7. Approximately what percent of strikeout leaders had 175 or more strikeouts during these years?

    7. _____

HOMEWORK For Questions 8 and 9, use the data in the table at the right.

Daily Homework Time		
Time (min)	Tally	Frequency
0–30	IIII I	6
31–60	IIII IIII II	12
61–90	IIII III	8
91–120	II	2

8. Display the set of data in a histogram.

    8.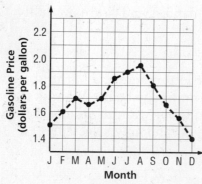

9. How many students spend more than 60 minutes doing homework each day?

    9. _____

10. **ECONOMICS** The graph shows the cost of gasoline per month. Redraw the graph so that it more accurately reflects the data.

    10.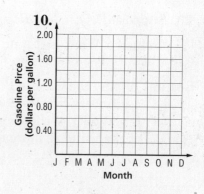

NAME _____ DATE _____ PERIOD _____

11. Two number cubes are rolled and a coin is tossed. Find the number of possible outcomes.

11. _____

12. What is the probability of winning a lottery game where the winning number is made up of 6 digits from 0 to 9 chosen at random?

12. _____

For Questions 13 and 14, tell whether each situation is a *permutation* or *combination*. Then solve.

13. There are 10 flowers in a vase. How many ways can you choose 4 of them?

13. _____

14. Nine goats are entered in the county fair. How many ways can the goats take first, second, and third place?

14. _____

15. How many ways can 12 runners come in first, and second places?

15. _____

16. How many 3 digit numbers can be formed if the first and second number must be 1 through 9 and the third number can be 0 through 9 and the first two numbers cannot be repeated?

16. _____

17. Five coins are dropped on the floor. Find the probability that they will all land heads up.

17. _____

18. Darla has written the numbers 1 to 8 on eight cards of the same size. She picks two cards at random, without replacing the first one. Find the probability of drawing cards with numbers that are multiples of 3.

18. _____

19. A 6-sided die is rolled. What is the probability of rolling a 1 or a prime number?

19. _____

20. Suppose $P(A) = \frac{1}{2}$, $P(B) = \frac{1}{3}$, and A and B are mutually exclusive. What is $P(A \text{ or } B)$?

20. _____

Bonus To play the Choose Four lottery game, a player selects 4 numbers from 1 to 35 on a play board. What is the probability of choosing all four winning numbers if each of the winning numbers is randomly selected?

B: _____

12 **Chapter 12 Test, Form 2D**

OLYMPICS Use the set of data at the right.

1. Display the set of data in a stem-and-leaf plot.

Olympic Medal Tally, Sydney, 2000			
Romania	26	Bulgaria	13
Korea	28	Greece	13
Hungary	17	Sweden	12
Poland	14	Norway	10
Japan	18	Ethiopia	8

Source: www.olympics.indya.com

1. _____

2. How many countries won more than 15 medals?

2. _____

3. Find the range and interquartile range for the set of data.

3. _____

4. How does the upper quartile of the data compare to the greatest value of the set?

4. _____

BASEBALL Use the set of data at the right.

5. Draw a box-and-whisker plot for the data.

6. Find the interquartile range.

MLB Home-Run Leaders			
2000	50	1995	50
1999	70	1994	43
1998	65	1993	46
1997	58	1992	43
1996	52	1991	44

Source: www.mlb.com

5.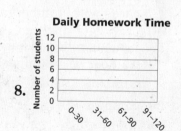

6. _____

7. Approximately what percent of home-run leaders had 50 or more runs during these years?

7. _____

HOMEWORK For Questions 8 and 9, use the data in the table at the right.

8. Display the set of data in a histogram.

Daily Homework Time		
Time (min)	Tally	Frequency
0–30	卌 II	7
31–60	卌 卌 I	11
61–90	卌 III	8
91–120	IIII	4

8.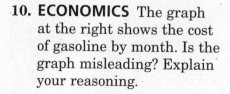

9. How many students spend more than 60 minutes doing homework each day?

9. _____

10. **ECONOMICS** The graph at the right shows the cost of gasoline by month. Is the graph misleading? Explain your reasoning.

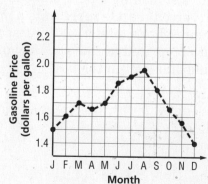

10. _____

Assessment

11. Two number cubes are rolled and two coins are tossed. Find the number of possible outcomes.

11. _____

12. What is the probability of winning a lottery game where the winning number is made up of 5 digits from 0 to 9 chosen at random?

12. _____

For Questions 13 and 14, tell whether each situation is a *permutation* or *combination*. Then solve.

13. There are 10 flowers in a vase. How many ways can you choose 5 of them?

13. _____

14. **FAIR** Eight sheep are entered in the county fair. How many ways can the sheep take first, second, third, and fourth place?

14. _____

15. How many ways can 4 runners come in first, second, and third places?

15. _____

16. How many 3 digit codes can be formed if each digit must be 0 through 9 and the digits cannot be repeated?

16. _____

17. Six coins are dropped on the floor. Find the probability that they will all land on tails.

17. _____

18. Mariko has written the numbers 1 to 6 on six cards of the same size. She picks two cards at random, without replacing the first one. Find the probability of drawing two cards with numbers less than 4.

18. _____

19. A die is rolled. What is the probability of rolling an even number or a number less than 5?

19. _____

20. Suppose $P(A) = \frac{1}{2}$, $P(B) = \frac{1}{3}$, and A and B are independent. What is $P(A \text{ and } B)$?

20. _____

Bonus Julie makes three out of 10 putts in miniature golf. To simulate her chances of making a putt, she puts 50 marbles in a box. A green marble represents a made putt, and a blue represents a missed putt. After a marble is drawn it is replaced in the box. How many blue marbles should Julie put in the box?

B: _____

12 **Chapter 12 Test, Form 3**

BASEBALL Use the information shown in the back-to-back stem-and-leaf plot.

MLB 2001 Games Won

National League		American League
8 8 6 2	6	2 3 5 6
9 6 3	7	3 5
8 8 6 6 2	8	0 2 3 5
3 3 2 0	9	1 5
	10	2
	11	6

$2|6 = 62$ games $7|3 = 73$ games
Source: www.mlb.com

1. What is the most games won by an American League team?

2. How many teams are in the National League?

3. What is the median number of games won by National League teams?

4. Compare the interquartile ranges for each league.

1. _____

2. _____

3. _____

4. _____

WEATHER Use the data shown in the table.

Average Monthly Precipitation for Seattle, WA (in.)											
Jan	Feb	Mar	Apr	May	Jun	Jul	Aug	Sep	Oct	Nov	Dec
5.4	4.0	3.8	2.5	1.8	1.6	0.9	1.2	1.9	3.3	5.6	6.0

Source: www.srh.noaa.gov

5. Draw a box-and-whisker plot for the data.

6. What percent of the months have precipitation averages of less than 4.7 inches?

5.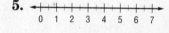

6. _____

VIDEOS For Questions 7–9, use the data in the histogram.

7. How many people rented fewer than 10 videos per month?

8. How many people were surveyed?

9. What percent of the people surveyed rent from four to nine videos per month?

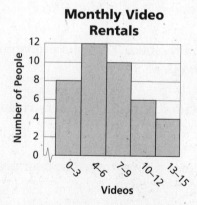

7. _____

8. _____

9. _____

10. The number of adults who see at least one movie per month is shown in the graph at the right. Is the graph misleading? Explain.

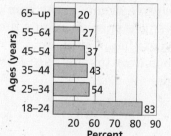

10. _____

12   Chapter 12 Test, Form 3   *(continued)*

11. A store sells three brands of gel pens. Each brand comes
in four different ink colors: blue, pink, purple, and green.
Kerry buys one of each brand and ink color. How many
pens does Kerry buy?

11. _____

12. A quiz has 10 true-false questions. How many answer keys
are possible?

12. _____

13. What is the probability of guessing a password that is made
up of four digits from 0 to 9 chosen at random?

13. _____

**For Questions 14–16, tell whether each situation is a
permutation or *combination*. Then solve.**

14. How many ways can 6 different apples be chosen from a
basket of 10 different apples?

14. _____

15. There are 8 swimmers in a race. How many ways can the
swimmers take 1st, 2nd, and 3rd place?

15. _____

16. In a door prize drawing, 3 numbers out of 10 are drawn at
random.

16. _____

17. Suppose $P(A) = \frac{3}{5}$, $P(B) = \frac{1}{3}$, and A and B are mutually
exclusive. What is $P(A$ and $B)$ and $P(A$ or $B)$?

17. _____

18. Six coins are dropped on the floor. Find the probability that
they will all land heads up.

18. _____

A coin is tossed and a 6-sided number cube is rolled.

19. Find the probability that a heads is tossed and a 5 is rolled.

19. _____

20. Find the probability that a tails is tossed and an even
number is rolled.

20. _____

Bonus Two *inclusive* events can happen at the same time. The
probability of two inclusive events is the sum of the
probability of each event happening minus the
probability of both events happening. Find
P(king or a heart) when drawing one card from a
standard deck of cards.

B: _____

12   Chapter 12 Extended-Response Test

Demonstrate your knowledge by giving a clear, concise solution to each problem. Be sure to include all relevant drawings and justify your answers. You may show your solution in more than one way or investigate beyond the requirements of the problem.

1. **a.** Name and describe two measures of variation.

   b. Produce a set of at least 8 pieces of data that has a lower quartile of 8 and a range of 14.

   c. Produce a set of 10 pieces of data that has a median of 25 and an interquartile range of 17.

   d. Display the data in part **c**, using a stem-and-leaf plot or a box-and-whisker plot. Tell what your display shows about the data.

2. Construct a misleading graph. Label the axes and give the graph a title. Explain why it is misleading.

3. Suppose you are a salesperson and wish to demonstrate to a customer all of the possible options you have available. Tell how you would do it. Use an example.

4. Probability is often used in baseball. Suppose Juan and Tony are the first two batters in the ninth inning. Their respective batting averages are 0.200 or 20% and 0.250 or 25%.

   a. Design a simulation to find the probability of both getting a hit.

   b. Tell how to find the probability of independent events. Find the probability of both getting a hit.

   c. What would the probability be of Juan or Tony getting a hit if they were mutually exclusive events? What would it be if they were not mutually exclusive events? Are the two events mutually exclusive? Why or why not?

Assessment

12 Standardized Test Practice

(Chapters 1-3)

Part 1: Multiple Choice

Instructions: Fill in the appropriate circle for the best answer.

1. Express 1500 in scientific notation. (Lesson 4–8)

   A 1.5×10^2 **B** 0.15×10^3 **C** 1.5×10^3 **D** 1.5×10^{-3} 1. Ⓐ Ⓑ Ⓒ Ⓓ

2. Find the amount of simple interest earned on $500 at an annual rate of
   $5\frac{1}{2}\%$ for 3 years. (Lesson 6–7)

   F $27.50   **G** $78   **H** $82.50   **J** $90   2. Ⓕ Ⓖ Ⓗ Ⓙ

3. Find the y-intercept of the graph of $2x - y = 10$. (Lesson 7–6)

   A 10   **B** 2   **C** −2   **D** −10   3. Ⓐ Ⓑ Ⓒ Ⓓ

4. What are the coordinates of the midpoint of the line segment
   with endpoints $J(0, -6)$ and $K(8, -4)$. (Lesson 9–6)

   F $(4, -5)$ **G** $(-2, 1)$ **H** $(4, -1)$ **J** $(-2, -5)$ 4. Ⓕ Ⓖ Ⓗ Ⓙ

5. If the measure of the hypotenuse of a right triangle is 15 meters
   and the measure of one leg is 9 meters, what is the measure of
   the other leg? (Lesson 9–4)

   A 306 m   **B** 144 m   **C** 12 m   **D** $\sqrt{306}$ m   5. Ⓐ Ⓑ Ⓒ Ⓓ

6. Classify the quadrilateral at the right with
   the name that best describes it. (Lesson 10–4)

   F square   **H** trapezoid
   G quadrilateral **J** parallelogram   6. Ⓕ Ⓖ Ⓗ Ⓙ

7. Find the volume of a rectangular prism with a length of
   5 meters, a width of 6 meters, and a height of 10 meters.
   (Lesson 11–2)

   A 600 m^3 **B** 300 m^3 **C** 150 m^3 **D** 75 m^3 7. Ⓐ Ⓑ Ⓒ Ⓓ

8. Find the surface area of a cone with a diameter of 11 meters and
   a slant height of 8.6 meters. (Lesson 11–5)

   F 148.6 m^2 **G** 243.6 m^2 **H** 392.2 m^2 **J** 677.3 m^2 8. Ⓕ Ⓖ Ⓗ Ⓙ

9. If the dimensions of a triangular prism are doubled, the volume
   (Lesson 11–6)

   A stays the same.   **C** is quadrupled.
   B is doubled.   **D** is 8 times greater.   9. Ⓐ Ⓑ Ⓒ Ⓓ

10. Three coins are tossed. How many outcomes are possible?
    (Lesson 12–6)

    F 12   **G** 9   **H** 8   **J** 6   10. Ⓕ Ⓖ Ⓗ Ⓙ

12 Standardized Test Practice (continued)

For Questions 11 and 12, use the box-and-whisker plot shown.
(Lessons 12–2 and 12–3)

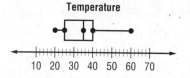

Temperature

10 20 30 40 50 60 70

11. Find the median.

A 20   C 35

B 25   D 40

11. Ⓐ Ⓑ Ⓒ Ⓓ

12. What is the lower quartile?

F 120   G 40   H 35   J 25

12. Ⓕ Ⓖ Ⓗ Ⓙ

13. A bag contains 3 red marbles, 4 green marbles, and 2 blue marbles. Kaya chooses a marble at random, then without replacing it chooses a second marble. What is the probability that Kaya chooses two green marbles? (Lesson 12–10)

A $\frac{59}{72}$ B $\frac{16}{81}$ C $\frac{1}{6}$ D $\frac{4}{27}$

13. Ⓐ Ⓑ Ⓒ Ⓓ

14. The coordinates of the endpoints of a segment are $E(-6, -2)$ and $F(-4, 8)$. What are the coordinates of the midpoint of this segment? (Lesson 9–5)

F $(-5, 3)$ G $(-10, 6)$ H $(-1, -5)$ J $(3, -5)$

14. Ⓕ Ⓖ Ⓗ Ⓙ

15. Find the surface area of a rectangular prism with length 5 cm, width 9 cm, and height 1 cm. (Lesson 11–4)

A 15 cm^2 B 30 cm^2 C 45 cm^2 D 118 cm^2

15. Ⓐ Ⓑ Ⓒ Ⓓ

16. Find the interquartile range for the quiz scores 45, 25, 60, 35, 20, 40, and 55. (Lesson 12–2)

F 10   G 15   H 30   J 40

16. Ⓕ Ⓖ Ⓗ Ⓙ

Part 2: Griddable

Instructions: Enter your answer by writing each digit of the answer in a column box and then shading in the appropriate circle that corresponds to that entry.

17. Find the area in square feet of a triangle with a base of 24 feet and a height of 18 feet. (Lesson 10–6)

17.

⓪	⓪	⓪	⓪		⓪	⓪
①	①	①	①		①	①
②	②	②	②		②	②
③	③	③	③		③	③
④	④	④	④		④	④
⑤	⑤	⑤	⑤		⑤	⑤
⑥	⑥	⑥	⑥		⑥	⑥
⑦	⑦	⑦	⑦		⑦	⑦
⑧	⑧	⑧	⑧		⑧	⑧
⑨	⑨	⑨	⑨		⑨	⑨

18. Find the value of 7!. (Lesson 12–9)

18.

⓪	⓪	⓪	⓪		⓪	⓪
①	①	①	①		①	①
②	②	②	②		②	②
③	③	③	③		③	③
④	④	④	④		④	④
⑤	⑤	⑤	⑤		⑤	⑤
⑥	⑥	⑥	⑥		⑥	⑥
⑦	⑦	⑦	⑦		⑦	⑦
⑧	⑧	⑧	⑧		⑧	⑧
⑨	⑨	⑨	⑨		⑨	⑨

Assessment

12 Standardized Test Practice *(continued)*

Part 3: Short Response

Instructions: Write your answer in the blank at the right of each question.

---

19. Display the set of data in a stem-and-leaf plot. (Lesson 12-1)

Top 10 Home Run Hitters NY Yankees, 2001	
Player	**Home Runs**
T. Martinez	34
B. Williams	26
J. Posada	22
D. Jeter	21
P. O'Neill	21
D. Justice	18
A. Soriano	18
S. Brosius	13
S. Spencer	10
C. Knoblauch	9

Source: www.yankees.mlb.com

19. _____

20. Weight measured in kilograms varies directly with the weight measured in pounds. If a car weighing 2000 pounds weighs about 900 kilograms, what is the rate of change for this direct variation equation and what does it represent? (Lesson 7-3)

20. _____

21. An algebra class had 36 students. Four of the students transferred to pre-algebra. What is the percent of change in the size of the algebra class? (Lesson 6–9)

21. _____

22. Find the slope and the y-intercept of the equation $6x - 2y = 14$. (Lesson 7-6)

22. _____

23. Suppose y varies directly with respect to x and the constant of variation is -5. What is the rate of change of this direct variation equation? (Lesson 7–4)

23. _____

24. At the same time a light pole casts a 5-foot shadow, a nearby 4.5-foot girl casts a 2-foot shadow. How tall is the light pole? (Lesson 9–6)

24. _____

25. A figure has vertices $A(3, 1)$, $B(-2, 0)$, $C(0, -4)$, and $D(2, -3)$. After a translation of 3 units right and 2 units down what are the coordinates of the new vertices? (Lesson 10–3)

25. _____

26. Identify a pair of skew lines in the figure at the right. (Lesson 11–1)

26. _____

27. Dien-Tu has 6 antique pocket watches. How many ways can he choose 3 watches to give to his 3 children? (Lesson 12–9)

27. _____

28. Ten students are applying to a math competition. How many ways can the school choose 4 students from these 10 students? (Lesson 12–9)

28. _____

29. Two number cubes are rolled. (Lesson 12–10)

   a. Find the probability of rolling a sum of 2.

29a. _____

   b. Find the probabilities of rolling each of the sums: 3, 4, 5, 6, 7, 8, 9, 10, 11, 12.

29b. _____

   c. What is the sum of the probabilities you found in parts a and b?

29c. _____

Answers (Anticipation Guide and Lesson 12-1)

12-1 Lesson Reading Guide
Stem-and-Leaf Plots

NAME _____ DATE _____ PERIOD _____

Get Ready for the Lesson

Read the introduction to Lesson 12-1 in your textbook. Write your answers below.

a. Is there an equal number of electors in each group? Explain.
   Sample answer: Even though the intervals are the same, the data are not distributed evenly as the number of pieces of data in each interval are not the same.

b. Name an advantage of displaying the data in groups.
   Sample answer: You can see how the data are distributed.

Read the Lesson 1–4. See students' work

Write a definition and give an example of each new vocabulary word or phrase.

Vocabulary	Definition	Example
1. stem-and-leaf plot		
2. stems		
3. leaves		
4. back-to-back stem-and-leaf plot		

Remember What You Learned

5. How will you remember which numbers of a stem-and-leaf plot represent the greater place value? Use the data to draw a back-to-back stem-and-leaf plot like actual leaves on stems. Read the data from the tree trunk and move outward.

Ages of Persons		
Apartment Building A	Apartment Building B	
33	16	19	39	21	20	1
26	23	11	10	21	36	37
34	24	37	32	22	11	2
17	29		10	1	32	38
			12	36	39	

Apartment A   Apartment B

0
1
2
3

Chapter 12   5   Glencoe Pre-Algebra

---

12 Anticipation Guide
Equations

NAME _____ DATE _____ PERIOD _____

Step 1 Before you begin Chapter 12

- Read each statement.
- Decide whether you Agree (A) or Disagree (D) with the statement.
- Write A or D in the first column OR if you are not sure whether you agree or disagree, write NS (Not Sure).

STEP 1 A, D, or NS	Statement	STEP 2 A or D
	1. A stem-and-leave plot organizes data in numerical order.	A
	2. It is always better to display data in a stem-and-leave plot than a table.	D
	3. The range of a set of data is the sum of the data divided by the number of items in the data set.	D
	4. A box-and-whisker plot usually contains a *box* with *whiskers* extending from each side.	A
	5. In a box-and-whisker plot, the median always divides the box in half.	D
	6. *Histogram* is another name for a bar graph.	D
	7. It does not matter which type of display is chosen for a set of data because all types show the same information.	D
	8. Two bar graphs for the same set of data can give different impressions about that data by using a different scale for each graph.	A
	9. Probability tells how likely an event is to occur.	A
	10. If the probability of an event is 30%, most likely that event will occur.	D
	11. A tree diagram can be used to count all possible outcomes in a problem.	A
	12. All probabilities range from 0 to 1.	A

Step 2 After you complete Chapter 12

- Reread each statement and complete the last column by entering an A (Agree) or a D (Disagree).
- Did any of your opinions about the statements change from the first column?
- For those statements that you mark with a D, use a separate sheet of paper to explain why you disagree. Use examples, if possible.

Chapter 12   3   Glencoe Pre-Algebra

Answers (Lesson 12-1)

NAME _____ DATE _____ PERIOD _____

12-1 Skills Practice
Stem-and-Leaf Plots

Display each set of data in a stem-and-leaf plot.

1. {7, 2, 3, 11, 20, 21, 17, 15, 15, 14}

Stem	Leaf
0	2 3 7
1	1 4 5 5 7
2	0 1

$0|3 = 3$

2. {8, 2, 14, 27, 7, 2, 16, 13, 29, 16}

Stem	Leaf
0	2 2 7 8
1	3 4 6 6
2	7 9

$1|4 = 14$

3.

Amount of Fresh Fruit Consumed per Person in the United States, 2002	
Fruit	Pounds Consumed per Person
Apples	16
Bananas	27
Cantaloupes	11
Grapefruit	5
Grapes	9
Oranges	11
Peaches and nectarines	5
Pears	3
Pineapples	4
Plums and prunes	1
Strawberries	5
Watermelons	14

Source: U.S. Census Bureau

Stem	Leaf
0	1 3 4 5 5 5 9
1	1 1 4 6
2	7

$0|3 = 3$

4.

Winning Scores in College Football Bowl Games, 2004	
Game and Winning School	Points Scored
Alamo Bowl, Nebraska	17
Fiesta Bowl, Ohio St.	35
Gator Bowl, Maryland	41
Holiday Bowl, Washington St.	28
Liberty Bowl, Utah	17
New Orleans Bowl, Memphis	27
Orange Bowl, Miami	16
Outback Bowl, Iowa	37
Peach Bowl, Clemson	27
Rose Bowl, Oklahoma	34
Sugar Bowl, Louisiana St.	21
Tangerine Bowl, N. Carolina St.	56

Source: footballabout.com

Stem	Leaf
1	6 7 7
2	1 7 7 8
3	4 5 7
4	1
5	6

$3|5 = 35$

HUMIDITY For Exercises 5–7, use the information in the back-to-back stem-and-leaf plot. Source: The New York Public Library Desk Reference

U.S. Average Relative Humidity (percent)		
Morning		Afternoon
	5	1 2 3 4 7 9
8 8 4	6	
9 4 0	8	7

$8|7 = 78\%$ ... $5|3 = 53\%$

5. What is the highest morning relative humidity? **89%**

6. What is the lowest afternoon relative humidity? **51%**

7. Does relative humidity tend to be higher in the morning or afternoon? **morning**

NAME _____ DATE _____ PERIOD _____

12-1 Study Guide and Intervention
Stem-and-Leaf Plots

Stem-and-Leaf Plot	**Words** One way to organize and display data is to use a **stem-and-leaf plot**. In a stem-and-leaf plot, numerical data are listed in ascending or descending order.

Model

Stem	Leaf
3	0 1 1 2 3 5 5 6 9
4	0 3 4 8 8

$3|7 = 37$

> The greatest place value of the data is used for the **stems**.

> The next greatest place value forms the **leaves**.

Example ZOOS Display the data shown at the right in a stem-and-leaf plot.

Step 1 The least and the greatest numbers are 55 and 95. The greatest place value digit in each number is in the tens. Draw a vertical line and write the stems from 5 to 9 to the left of the line.

Step 2 Write the leaves to the right of the line, with the corresponding stem. For example, for 85, write 5 to the right of 8.

Step 3 Rearrange the leaves so they are ordered from least to greatest. Then include a key or an explanation.

Size of U. S. Zoos	
Zoo	Size (acres)
Audubon (New Orleans)	58
Cincinnati	85
Dallas	95
Denver	80
Houston	55
Los Angeles	80
Oregon	64
St. Louis	90
San Francisco	75
Woodland Park (Seattle)	92

Stem	Leaf
5	5 8
6	4
7	5
8	0 0 5
9	0 2 5

$8|5 = 85$ acres

Exercises

Display each set of data in a stem-and-leaf plot.

1. {27, 35, 39, 27, 24, 33, 18, 19}

Stem	Leaf
1	8 9
2	4 7 7
3	3 5 9

$2|4 = 24$

2. {94, 83, 88, 77, 95, 99, 88, 87}

Stem	Leaf
7	7
8	3 7 8 8
9	4 5 9

$8|5 = 85$

ROLLER COASTERS For Exercises 3 and 4, use the stem-and-leaf plot shown.

The Fastest Roller Coasters	
Stem	Leaf
8	3 5
9	0 5
10	0

$8|3 = 83$ mph

3. What is the speed of the fastest roller coaster? The slowest? **100 mph; 83 mph**

4. What is the median speed? **92 mph**

Answers (Lesson 12-1)

12-1 Practice

Stem-and-Leaf Plots

NAME   DATE   PERIOD

Display each set of data in a stem-and-leaf plot.

1. {68, 63, 70, 59, 78, 64, 68, 73, 61, 66, 70}

Stem	Leaf
5	9
6	1 3 4 6 8 8
7	0 0 3 8

6 | 4 = 64

2. {27, 32, 42, 31, 36, 37, 47, 23, 39, 31, 41, 38, 30, 34, 29, 42, 37}

Stem	Leaf
2	3 7 9
3	0 1 1 2 4 6 7 7 8 9
4	1 2 2 7

3 | 6 = 36

3.

Major League Baseball Leading Pitchers, 2005

Player and Team	Wins
C. Capuano	18
C. Carpenter	21
B. Colon	21
J. Garland	18
R. Johnson	17
C. Lee	18
J. Lieber	17
R. Oswalt	20
A. Pettitte	17
D. Willis	22

Source: sports.espn.go.com

Stem	Leaf
1	7 7 7 8 8 8
2	0 1 1 2

1 | 8 = 18

4.

Average Prices Received by U.S. Farmers, 2004

Commodity	Price (dollars per 100 pounds)
Beef Cattle	86
Hogs	49
Lambs	101
Milk	16
Veal Calves	119

Source: U.S Department of Agriculture

Stem	Leaf
1	6
2	
3	
4	9
5	
6	
7	
8	6
9	
10	1
11	9

6 | 1 = $63 per 100 lbs

RECREATION For Exercises 5–7, use the information in the back-to-back stem-and-leaf plot shown at the right.

5. The category with the lowest total expenditure in 1992 was motion pictures. What was its total? **$5 billion**

6. What is the median total recreational spending for 1992? For 2002? **$17.5 billion; $34.5 billion**

7. Compare the total spending on recreation in 1992 with that in 2002. In general, spending on recreation increases between 1992 and 2002.

Total U.S. Spending on Personal Recreation (by Category)

1992	Stem	2002
7 5 5 0	0	9
8 7 2 0 1	1	0 2 8
	2	0 3 4 5 7
4 0 3	3	4 4
	4	4
	5	6 0
1 6 0	6	
	7	
	8	4
	9	

7 | 2 = $27 billion   3 | 5 = $35 billion

12-1 Word Problem Practice

Stem-and-Leaf Plots

NAME   DATE   PERIOD

1. CUSTOMER SERVICE A restaurant owner recorded the average time in minutes customers waited to be seated each night. His data are shown in the table below. To organize the data into a stem-and-leaf plot, how many stems would you need?

Week 1	15	8	10	5	20	35	45
Week 2	9	3	7	8	25	38	43

5

2. PHONE Allison's mother makes a stem-and-leaf plot to track the time in minutes that Allison spends talking on the phone each night. In which interval are most of the Allison's calls?

Stem	Leaf
1	0 5
2	3 4 5 8 9
3	0 5 8
4	1 3 5

1 | 5 = 15 minutes

20–29 minutes

3. ELECTRIC BILLS Jenny's family is selling their house. Jenny's mother wants to put together a table of monthly electricity costs. Below is a list of their electric bills for the past twelve months. Organize the data in a stem-and-leaf plot. In which interval are most of the electric bills?

$95, $99, $85, $79, $82, $88, $98, $95, $94, $87, $89, $90

Stem	Leaf
7	9
8	2 5 7 8 9
9	0 4 5 5 8 9

Most of the electric bills are in the $90–$99 interval.

4. TEST SCORES The scores from the most recent test in Mr. James' biology class are shown in the stem-and-leaf plot below. Find the highest and lowest scores, and then write a statement that describes the data.

Stem	Leaf
5	4 5
6	3 7 8
7	0 1 5 5 8 9
8	0 2 3 7 9
9	0 3 5 8 8

5 | 4 = 54%

lowest: 54, highest: 98; Sample answer: 16 out 21 students scored 70% or better on the test.

SPORTS For Exercises 5–7, use the following information.

Tamara and LaDawn have recorded their times in seconds in the 100-meter dash from the past six track meets in the table below.

LaDawn	16.5	16.6	17.0	16.8	17.2	17.1
Tamara	16.7	16.4	16.1	17.0	16.5	16.8

5. Organize the times in a back-to-back stem-and-leaf plot.

LaDawn		Tamara
8 6 5	16	1 4 5 7 8
2 1 0	17	0

16 | 2 = 16.2 seconds

6. What are the median times for LaDawn and for Tamara?

LaDawn: 16.9 s, Tamara: 16.6 s

7. If you were the coach, who would you choose to represent the team at the next competition? Explain. **Tamara, because her median time is faster.**

Answers (Lesson 12-1)

NAME _____ DATE _____ PERIOD _____

12-1 Graphing Calculator Activity

Stem-and-Leaf Plots

The graphing calculator can be used to help make stem-and-leaf plots.

Example **Make a stem-and-leaf plot from the ages of the U.S. Presidents at their deaths.**

67 90 83 85 73 80 78 79 68 71 53 65 74 64 77 56 66 63 70
49 56 71 67 71 58 60 72 67 57 60 90 63 88 78 46 64 81 93

Source: *The World Almanac*

Before entering the data into the lists, clear the lists of previous data. Enter the data in L1. Next, use the sort feature of the calculator to place the data in ascending order. Then, use the sorted list to create a stem-and-leaf plot.

Keystrokes: STAT 4 2nd [L1] STAT ENTER 67 ENTER 90 ENTER 83 ENTER 85 ENTER ... 46 ENTER 64 ENTER 81 ENTER STAT 2 2nd [L1])
ENTER STAT ENTER ▶

Stem	Leaf
4	6 9
5	3 6 6 7 8
6	0 0 3 3 4 4 5 6 7 7 7 8
7	0 1 1 1 2 3 4 7 8 8 9
8	0 1 3 5 8
9	0 0 3

4|6 = 46

Exercises

Create a stem-and-leaf plot for each set of data.

1. 83 65 89 88 72 70 66 65 71 64 81 83 84 83
82 64 72 75 88 67 72 81 70 67 89 72 81 70

Stem	Leaf
6	4 5 5 6 7 7
7	0 0 0 1 2 2 2 2 5
8	1 1 1 2 3 3 3 4 8 8 9 9

6|4 = 64

2. 13.8 14.8 14.3 12.7 12.2 13.9 11.8 10.2 15.7
12.1 13.3 13.6 11.4 12.2 12.7 12.8 14.3 14.4

Stem	Leaf
10	2
11	4 8
12	1 2 2 7 7 8
13	3 6 8 9
14	3 3 4 8
15	7

6|4 = 64

3. Press STAT ENTER to verify that the data from Exercise 2 is in L1. Then press 2 2nd [L1] . 0) STO▶ 2nd [L2] ENTER 10 MATH ▶ 3 2nd [L1] STO▶ 2nd [L3] ENTER STAT 1. Compare the lists displayed on the calculator. **The data in L2 is the data from L1 rounded to the nearest whole number and the data in L3 is 10 times that of the data in L2.**

Chapter 12   11   Glencoe Pre-Algebra

NAME _____ DATE _____ PERIOD _____

12-1 Enrichment

U.S. Presidents

The political parties in our country have changed over time. At the time of our nation's founding, the Federalist and Democratic-Republican parties were the nationally prominent parties. In recent years, all U.S. Presidents have been from either the Republican or Democratic Party.

1. Make a table to display the data for the number of U.S. Presidents from each political party.

Party	Number of Presidents
Republican	18
Democrat	13
Federalist	2
Democratic-Republican	4
Whig	4
Union	1

Republican	Democrat	Federalist
Abraham Lincoln	Andrew Jackson	George Washington
Ulysses S. Grant	Martin Van Buren	John Adams
Rutherford B. Hayes	James K. Polk	**Democratic-Republican**
James A. Garfield	Franklin Pierce	Thomas Jefferson
Chester A. Arthur	James Buchanan	James Madison
Benjamin Harrison	Grover Cleveland	James Monroe
William McKinley	Woodrow Wilson	John Quincy Adams
Theodore Roosevelt	Franklin D. Roosevelt	**Whig**
William Howard Taft	Harry S Truman	William Henry Harrison
Warren G. Harding	John F. Kennedy	John Tyler
Calvin Coolidge	Lyndon B. Johnson	Zachary Taylor
Herbert Hoover	Jimmy Carter	Millard Fillmore
Dwight D. Eisenhower	Bill Clinton	**Union**
Richard Nixon		Andrew Johnson
Gerald Ford		
Ronald Reagan		
George Bush		
George W. Bush		

2. Display the data from the table in a stem-and-leaf plot.

Number of Presidents from Each Party

Stem	Leaf
0	1 2 4 4
1	3 8

1|3 = 13

3. What is the difference in the number of presidents from the party with the most presidents and the party with the fewest presidents? **18 − 1 = 17**

4. What is another type of information about U.S. Presidents that could be displayed using a stem-and-leaf plot?

Sample answers: how old they were when elected president

Chapter 12   10   Glencoe Pre-Algebra

Answers (Lesson 12-2)

12-2 Study Guide and Intervention

NAME _____ DATE _____ PERIOD _____

Measures of Variation

The **range** and the **interquartile range** describe how a set of data varies.

Term	Definition
range	The difference between the greatest and the least values of the set
median	The value that separates the data set in half
lower quartile	The median of the lower half of a set of data
upper quartile	The median of the upper half of a set of data
interquartile range	The difference between the upper quartile and the lower quartile
outlier	Data that is more than 1.5 times the value of the interquartile range beyond the quartiles.

Example Find the range, interquartile range, and any outliers for each set of data.

a. {3, 12, 17, 2, 21, 14, 14, 8}

Step 1 List the data from least to greatest. The range is $21 - 2$ or 19. Then find the median.

2 3 8 12 14 14 17 21

$$\text{median} = \frac{14 + 12}{2} \text{ or } 13$$

Step 2 Find the upper and lower quartiles.

2 3 8 12 14 14 17 21

$$LQ = \frac{3 + 8}{2} \text{ or } 5.5 \qquad UQ = \frac{14 + 17}{2} \text{ or } 15.5$$

The interquartile range is $15.5 - 5.5$ or 10. There are no outliers.

b.

Stem	Leaf
2	2 6 9
3	1 1 3 4 9
4	0 2 5 5 7 7 8
5	3 4 6 6

$3 \mid 4 = 34$

The stem-and-leaf plot displays the data in order. The greatest value is 56. The least value is 22. So, the range is $56 - 22$ or 34.

The median is 42. The LQ is 31 and the UQ is 48. So, the interquartile range is $48 - 31$ or 17.

There are no outliers.

Exercises

WEATHER For Exercises 1 and 2, use the data in the stem-and-leaf plot at the right.

1. Find the range, median, upper quartile, lower quartile, interquartile range, and any outliers for each set of data. **July lows: range: 30°F; median: 73; UQ: 76; LQ: 59; interquartile range: 17°F; July highs: range: 43°F; median: 83; UQ: 91; LQ: 79; interquartile range: 12°F**

2. Write a sentence that compares the data. **July highs vary more widely than July lows.**

Average Extreme July Temperatures in World Cities

Low Temps.		High Temps.
9 1 1 0	5	
	6	4 7 9
9 8 6 5 4 3 0 0	7	9
	8	1 1 3 3 4 8
	9	0 1 2 5
	10	7

$0 \mid 8 = 80°F \qquad 7 \mid 9 = 79°F$

12-2 Lesson Reading Guide

NAME _____ DATE _____ PERIOD _____

Measures of Variation

Get Ready for the Lesson

Read the introduction to Lesson 12-2 in your textbook. Write your answers below.

a. What is the fastest speed? **173 mph**

b. What is the slowest speed? **134 mph**

c. Find the difference between these two speeds. **39 mph**

d. Write a sentence comparing the fastest winning average speed and the slowest winning average speed. **The fastest winning average speed and the slowest winning average speed are within 39 miles per hour of each other.**

Read the Lesson 1–7. See students' work.

Write a definition and give an example of each new vocabulary word or phrase.

Vocabulary	Definition	Example
1. measures of variation		
2. range		
3. quartiles		
4. lower quartile		
5. upper quartile		
6. interquartile range		
7. outlier		

Remember What You Learned

7. Complete the following diagram by filling in the boxes with the appropriate vocabulary words.

Diagram Title: **Measures of Variation**

1 2 4 6 7 9 11 16 17 20 21 21 30

range

lower quartile

upper quartile

interquartile range

NAME _____ DATE _____ PERIOD _____

12-2 Practice

Measures of Variation

Find the range, interquartile range, and any outliers for each set of data.

1. {3, 9, 11, 8, 6, 12, 5, 4}
9; 5.5

2. {8, 3, 9, 14, 12, 11, 20, 23, 5, 26}
23; 12

3. {42, 50, 46, 47, 38, 41}
12; 6

4. {10.3, 9.8, 10.1, 16.2, 18.0, 11.4, 16.0, 15.8}
8.2; 5.9

5. {107, 82, 93, 112, 120, 95, 98, 56, 109, 110}
64; 17; 56 is an outlier.

6. {106, 103, 112, 109, 115, 118, 113, 108}
15; 7

7.
Stem	Leaf
1	7 8
2	2 3 5 6 8
3	0

2|2 = 22
13; 7

8.
Stem	Leaf
5	6 7
6	0 1 1 4 8 8 9
7	0 2 3 5 6 7

6|1 = 61
21; 12

9.
Stem	Leaf
4	0 0 0 2 5 7
5	2 6
6	1 8 8
7	0 1 9

5|2 = 52
39; 26

10.
Stem	Leaf
6	4 7 9
7	9
8	1 1 3 3 4 6
9	0 1 2 5

7|9 = 79
31; 11

11.
Stem	Leaf
4	4
5	2
6	
7	3 3
8	9

5|2 = 52
59; 39.5

12.
Stem	Leaf
4	3 3 5 7 9
5	0 0 1
6	2
7	4 4 6 8
8	
9	0 1 1 2 2 5

5|1 = 51
52; 42

POPULATION For Exercises 13–15, use the data in the table at the right.

13. What is the range of populations shown? **13.8 million**

14. What is the interquartile range for the annual growth rate? **1.3%**

15. Where does the city with the fastest growth rate fall in terms of population? The city with the slowest growth rate? **near the median; at the LQ**

Populations of the World's Largest Cities 2000		
City	Population (millions)	Annual Growth Rate (%)
Tokyo, Japan	26.4	0.51
Mexico City, Mexico	18.1	1.81
Mumbai, India	18.1	3.54
Sao Paulo, Brazil	17.8	1.43
New York City, U.S.	16.6	0.37
Lagos, Nigeria	13.4	5.33
Los Angeles, U.S.	13.1	1.15
Calcutta, India	12.9	1.60
Shanghai, China	12.9	−0.35
Buenos Aires, Argentina	12.6	1.14

Source: World Almanac

NAME _____ DATE _____ PERIOD _____

12-2 Skills Practice

Measures of Variation

Find the range, interquartile range, and any outliers for each set of data.

1. {7, 9, 21, 8, 13, 19}
14; 11

2. {33, 34, 27, 40, 38, 35}
13; 5

3. {37, 29, 42, 33, 31, 36, 40}
13; 9

4. {87, 72, 104, 94, 85, 71, 80, 98}
33; 20

5. {92, 89, 124, 114, 98, 118, 115, 106, 101, 149}
60; 20; 149 is an outlier.

6. {6.7, 3.4, 3.8, 4.2, 5.1, 5.8, 6.0, 4.5}
3.3; 1.9

7. {4.3, 1.9, 6.3, 5.1, 2.1, 1.6, 2.4, 5.6, 5.9, 3.5}
4.7; 3.5

8. {127, 58, 49, 101, 104, 98, 189, 111}
140; 41; 189 is an outlier.

9.
Stem	Leaf
1	0 0 3 8 9
2	0 5
3	1 2 4

2|0 = 20
24; 18

10.
Stem	Leaf
7	8 9
8	1 3 7
9	3 5 6

9|3 = 93
18; 14

11.
Stem	Leaf
1	0 2 3 6 8 9
2	2 2 5
3	6
4	2 3 4

1|5 = 15
32; 22

12.
Stem	Leaf
0	1 1 3 3 7 9
1	2 6 7 8 9 9
2	0 1 2 2 4 5 7 9 9 9
3	2 4 6 7 8
4	0 1 3

2|0 = 20
42; 16

13.
Stem	Leaf
6	0 6
7	1
8	4 9 9
9	1 3 7 7 7 8

8|4 = 84
38; 19.5

14.
Stem	Leaf
4	8
5	1 2 4 7 7
6	0 2 5
7	4

6|2 = 62
26; 10

HEALTH For Exercises 15–17, use the data in the table showing the calories burned by a 125-pound person.

15. What is the range of the data? **420 Calories**

16. What is the interquartile range of the data? **285 Calories**

17. Are there any outliers? **No.**

18. Which activity burns the most calories per hour? The least calories per hour? **running; yoga**

Estimated Calories Burned	
Activity	Calories Burned per Hour
Basketball	480
Bicycling	600
Hiking	360
Mowing the Lawn	270
Running	660
Soccer	420
Swimming	600
Weight Training	360
Yoga	240

Source: www.fitresource.com

12-2 Word Problem Practice

Measures of Variation

NAME _____ DATE _____ PERIOD _____

1. SUSPENSION BRIDGES The lengths in meters of the world's largest suspension bridges are given in the table below. Find the range of the data.

Suspension Bridge	Length of center span (meters)
Akashi-Kaikyo Bridge	1991
Great Belt Bridge	1624
Runyang Bridge	1490
Humber Bridge	1410
Jiangyin Suspension Bridge	1385
Tsing Ma Bridge	1377
Verrazano Narrows Bridge	1298
Golden Gate Bridge	1280
Hoga Kusten Bridge	1210
Mackinac Bridge	1158

833

2. ACADEMICS Mrs. Santiago gave each of her 21 students a reading test. The scores are organized in the stem-and-leaf plot below. Find the median score.

Stem	Leaf
1	5 7 8 9
2	0 2 5 5 5 7 8
3	0 2 5 7 9
4	2 4 5 8 9
5	0

2|5 5.25

30

3. EXERCISE Shown below is the number of minutes Yashika walked each day for two weeks. Find the upper and lower quartile of the data.

Week 1	25	22	15	30	45	20	18	25
Week 2	35	42	30	25	20	15	10	

lower quartile: 18; upper quartile: 30

4. BASKETBALL Jan tracked the points per game of his favorite basketball player for the 2004–2005 season. During the last six games that he played in the season, he scored these points: 42, 18, 20, 33, 22, 37. Find the upper and lower quartiles, the interquartile range, and determine if there are any outliers.

lower quartile: 20, upper quartile: 37; interquartile range: 17; There are no outliers.

SPORTS For Exercises 5–7, use the following information.

Rodney researched the longest-playing professional baseball players. He made a table of the nine who have played professional baseball for 25 seasons or more.

Player	Years Played
Eddie Collins	25
Cap Anson	27
Jim Kaat	25
Bobby Wallace	25
Tommy John	26
Charlie Hough	27
Rickey Henderson	25
Deacon McGuire	26
Nolan Ryan	27

Source: www.baseballreference.com

5. Find the range of the data set.
2

6. What is the median of the data set?
26

7. Find the upper and lower quartile and the interquartile range.
lower quartile:25, upper quartile: 27; interquartile range: 2

12-2 Enrichment

NAME _____ DATE _____ PERIOD _____

Variance

Another way to measure the variation of a set of data is by computing the **variance**. The higher the variance is for a group of numbers, the more "spread out" the data will be.

The table below shows the price of the stock for two companies during one week.

	Monday	Tuesday	Wednesday	Thursday	Friday
Acme Computer Systems	$10	$7	$3	$8	$12
Baker Pencil Company	$7	$8	$7	$9	$9

Computing the variance will show which company's stock has the greater variation. To compute the variance, follow these steps:

Step 1 Subtract the mean from each number in the set.

Step 2 Multiply each difference in step 1 by itself.

Step 3 Add these differences.

Step 4 Divide the total by the number of members of the set.

Example **Find the variance for Acme Computer Systems.**
The mean average price for the week for each company is $8.

$(10 - 8) \times (10 - 8) + (7 - 8) \times (7 - 8) + (3 - 8) \times (3 - 8) + (8 - 8) \times (8 - 8) + (12 - 8) \times (12 - 8)$

$4 \quad + \quad 1 \quad + \quad 25 \quad + \quad 0 \quad + \quad 16 \quad = 46$

The variance is $46 \div 5$, or 9.2.

Exercises

Solve.

1. Do you think the variance for Baker Pencil Company will be higher than the variance for Acme Computer Systems? Why? Compute the variance for Baker Pencil Company to see whether you are correct. **No; the prices are closer together; 0.8**

2. Consolidated Airlines also had an average price last week of $8 per share, but its variance was 10.8. Indicate five stock prices that could produce this variance. (*Hint:* Change only the Monday and Tuesday prices for Acme.) **Answers may vary. Sample answer: $11, $6, $3, $8, $12**

3. Sleepy Mattress Company's stock had an average price last week of $8 per share and a variance of 0. What was the price of shares each day last week? **$8 each day**

4. Are there any values that the variance cannot equal? If so, what are these values? **yes; values less than zero**

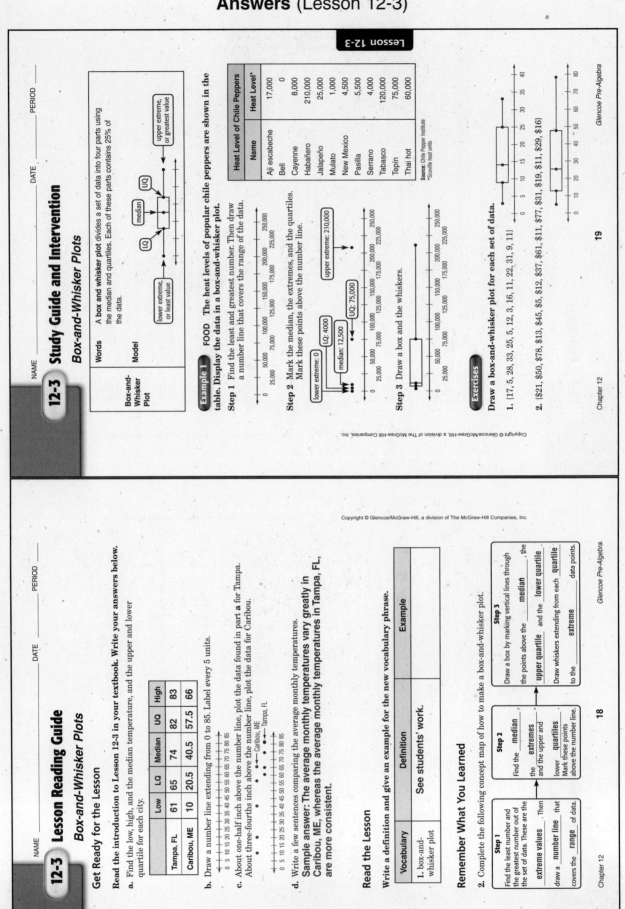

12-3 Study Guide and Intervention
Box-and-Whisker Plots

Lesson 12-3

Words	A box and whisker plot divides a set of data into four parts using the median and quartiles. Each of these parts contains 25% of the data.
Box-and-Whisker Plot	**Model**

Example 1 FOOD The heat levels of popular chile peppers are shown in the table. Display the data in a box-and-whisker plot.

Heat Level of Chile Peppers	
Name	**Heat Level***
Ají escabeche	17,000
Bell	0
Cayenne	8,000
Habañero	210,000
Jalapeño	25,000
Mulato	1,000
New Mexico	4,500
Pasilla	5,500
Serrano	4,000
Tabasco	120,000
Tepin	75,000
Thai hot	60,000

Source: Chile Pepper Institute
*Scoville heat units

Step 1 Find the least and greatest number. Then draw a number line that covers the range of the data.

Step 2 Mark the median, the extremes, and the quartiles. Mark these points above the number line.

Step 3 Draw a box and the whiskers.

Exercises

Draw a box-and-whisker plot for each set of data.

1. {17, 5, 28, 33, 25, 5, 12, 3, 16, 11, 22, 31, 9, 11}

2. {$21, $50, $78, $13, $45, $5, $12, $37, $61, $11, $77, $31, $19, $11, $29, $16}

Chapter 12   19   Glencoe Pre-Algebra

12-3 Lesson Reading Guide
Box-and-Whisker Plots

Get Ready for the Lesson

Read the introduction to Lesson 12-3 in your textbook. Write your answers below.

a. Find the low, high, and the median temperature, and the upper and lower quartile for each city.

	Low	LQ	Median	UQ	High
Tampa, FL	61	65	74	82	83
Caribou, ME	10	20.5	40.5	57.5	66

b. Draw a number line extending from 0 to 85. Label every 5 units.

c. About one-half inch above the number line, plot the data found in part a for Tampa. About three-fourths inch above the number line, plot the data for Caribou.

d. Write a few sentences comparing the average monthly temperatures.
Sample answer: The average monthly temperatures vary greatly in Caribou, ME, whereas the average monthly temperatures in Tampa, FL, are more consistent.

Read the Lesson

Write a definition and give an example for the new vocabulary phrase.

Vocabulary	Definition	Example
1. box-and-whisker plot	See students' work.	

Remember What You Learned

2. Complete the following concept map of how to make a box-and-whisker plot.

Step 1
Find the least number and the greatest number out of the set of data. These are the **extreme values**. Then draw a **number line** that covers the **range** of data.

Step 2
Find the **median**, the **extremes** and the upper and lower **quartiles**. Mark these points above the number line.

Step 3
Draw a box by marking vertical lines through the points above the **median**, the **upper quartile** and the **lower quartile**. Draw whiskers extending from each **quartile** to the **extreme** data points.

Chapter 12   18   Glencoe Pre-Algebra

Answers (Lesson 12-3)

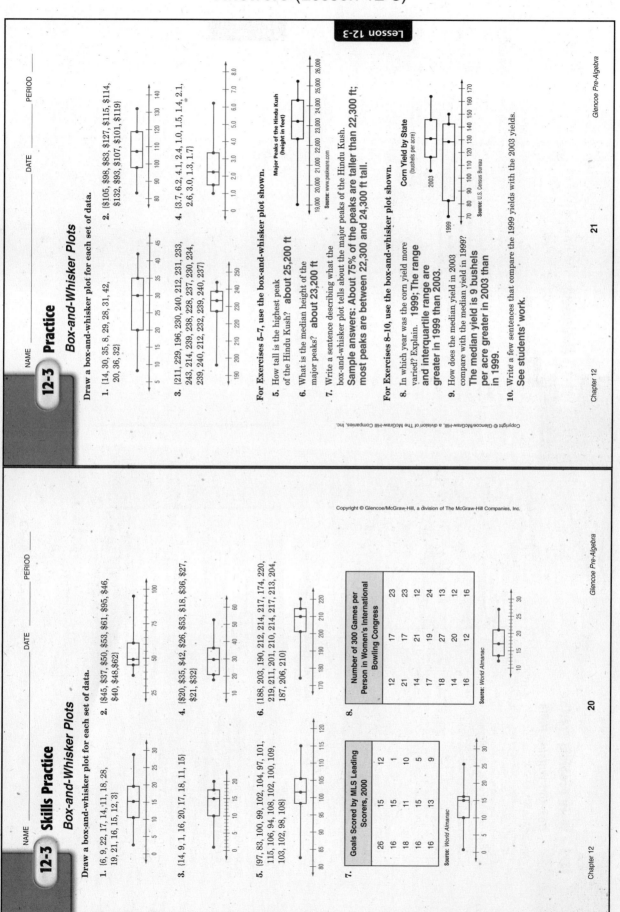

12-3 Skills Practice

Box-and-Whisker Plots

Draw a box-and-whisker plot for each set of data.

1. {6, 9, 22, 17, 14, 11, 18, 28, 19, 21, 16, 15, 12, 3}

2. {$45, $37, $50, $53, $61, $95, $46, $40, $48, $62}

3. {14, 9, 1, 16, 20, 17, 18, 11, 15}

4. {$20, $35, $42, $26, $53, $18, $36, $27, $21, $32}

5. {97, 83, 100, 99, 102, 104, 97, 101, 115, 106, 94, 108, 102, 100, 109, 103, 102, 98, 108}

6. {188, 203, 190, 212, 214, 217, 174, 220, 219, 211, 201, 210, 214, 217, 213, 204, 187, 206, 210}

7.
Goals Scored by MLS Leading Scorers, 2000	
26	15	12
16	15	1
18	11	10
16	15	5
16	13	9

Source: *World Almanac*

8.
Number of 300 Games per Person in Women's International Bowling Congress		
12	17	23
21	17	23
14	21	12
17	19	24
18	27	13
14	20	12
16	12	16

Source: *World Almanac*

Chapter 12   20   *Glencoe Pre-Algebra*

12-3 Practice

Box-and-Whisker Plots

Draw a box-and-whisker plot for each set of data.

1. {14, 30, 35, 8, 29, 28, 31, 42, 20, 36, 32}

2. {$105, $98, $83, $127, $115, $114, $132, $93, $107, $101, $119}

3. {211, 229, 196, 230, 240, 212, 231, 233, 243, 214, 239, 238, 228, 237, 230, 234, 239, 240, 212, 232, 239, 240, 237}

4. {3.7, 6.2, 4.1, 2.4, 1.0, 1.5, 1.4, 2.1, 2.6, 3.0, 1.3, 1.7}

For Exercises 5–7, use the box-and-whisker plot shown.

5. How tall is the highest peak of the Hindu Kush? **about 25,200 ft**

6. What is the median height of the major peaks? **about 23,200 ft**

7. Write a sentence describing what the box-and-whisker plot tells about the major peaks of the Hindu Kush. **Sample answers: About 75% of the peaks are taller than 22,300 ft; most peaks are between 22,300 and 24,300 ft tall.**

Major Peaks of the Hindu Kush (height in feet)

Source: www.peakware.com

For Exercises 8–10, use the box-and-whisker plot shown.

8. In which year was the corn yield more varied? Explain. **1999; The range and interquartile range are greater in 1999 than 2003.**

9. How does the median yield in 2003 compare with the median yield in 1999? **The median yield is 9 bushels per acre greater in 2003 than in 1999.**

10. Write a few sentences that compare the 1999 yields with the 2003 yields. **See students' work.**

Corn Yield by State (bushels per acre)

Source: U.S. Census Bureau

Chapter 12   21   *Glencoe Pre-Algebra*

Answers (Lesson 12-3)

12-3 Word Problem Practice

Box-and-Whisker Plots

1. CARS Martina bought a new car and wanted to know how many miles per gallon her new car got. She kept track of her mileage and gas consumption for 10 separate trips. The miles per gallon are displayed in the box-and-whisker plot below. What is the median of the data?

20 22 24 26 28 30 32 34 36 38 40

36 mpg

2. ZOOLOGY Archie researched pandas for a science project. He looked up the weight in kilograms of adult pandas and displayed the data in a box-and-whisker plot. How much do most adult pandas weigh?

80 88 96 104 112 120

between 90 and 115 kg

3. SPORTS The number of games won by the teams in each conference of the National Basketball League is displayed below. Write a few sentences that compare the data.

Eastern Conference

Western Conference

10 20 30 40 50 60 70

Sample answer: The least number of games won in the Eastern Conference was 13, and the least number of games won in the Western Conference was 18.

4. FOOD The table shows the recent top 10 ice cream-consuming countries. Make a box-and-whisker plot of the data.

Country	Consumption per Capita (pints)
Australia	36.8
New Zealand	27.8
USA	27.5
Sweden	23.8
Canada	22.2
Ireland	20.6
Norway	20.2
Finland	19.4
Denmark	16.9
Germany	16.7

16 18 20 22 24 26 28 30 32 34 36 38

WEATHER For Exercises 5–7, use the information below.

George researched peak wind gusts in Texas. He made a box-and-whisker plot to display the data he collected.

50 60 70 80 90 100

5. What is the slowest recorded wind gust?

54 mph

6. What percent of the wind gusts range from 67 to 82 miles per hour? **50%**

7. What would a peak gust have to be for it to be an outlier? **Sample answer: Either much lower than 44.5 mph or much greater than 104.5 mph**

12-3 Enrichment

Traffic Safety Facts

Primary enforcement seatbelt laws allow law enforcement officers to pull over drivers and ticket them for not wearing a seatbelt as they would for any other violation. Secondary seatbelt laws allow the driver to be ticketed for not wearing a seatbelt only if they are stopped for another violation of the law. The table to the right lists several states with seat belt laws and the estimated seatbelt use rates.

Type of Safety Belt Law	State	Seatbelt Use Rate (%)
Primary	Texas	76.1
Primary	Oklahoma	67.9
Secondary	Arkansas	54.5
Primary	Louisiana	68.1
Secondary	Nevada	74.5
Primary	California	91.1
Primary	Hawaii	82.5

Source: National Highway Traffic Safety Administration

1. Make a box-and-whisker plot of the seatbelt use rates.

52 56 60 64 68 72 76 80 84 88 92

a. What are the upper and lower quartiles?

UQ- 82.5, LQ- 67.9

b. What is the median seatbelt use rate?

median–74.5

2. Make a back-to-back stem-and-leaf plot to compare the seatbelt use rates in states with primary seatbelt laws to those states with secondary seat belt laws.

Sample answer:

Primary		Secondary
	5	45
	6	
7.9 7.8	6.1	7	45
2.5	8	
1.1	9	
	5	45 5 54.5%

3. What conclusion can you make from the plot in Exercise 2?

Those with primary laws have a greater seatbelt use.

NAME _____ DATE _____ PERIOD _____

12-4 Study Guide and Intervention

Histograms

Histograms
A histogram uses bars to display numerical data that have been organized into equal intervals.
- There is no space between bars.
- Because the intervals are equal, all of the bars have the same width.
- Intervals with a frequency of 0 have no bar.

Example **ELEVATIONS** The frequency table shows the highest elevations in each state. Display the data in a histogram.

Highest Elevation in Each State

Elevation (ft)	Tally	Frequency
0–3999	卌 卌 卌 卌 II	22
4000–7999	卌 卌 IIII	14
8000–11,999	II	2
12,000–15,999	卌 卌 I	11
16,000–19,999		0
20,000–23,999	I	1

Source: www.peakware.com

Highest Elevation in Each State

Step 1 Draw and label the axes as shown. Include the title.

Step 2 Show the frequency intervals on the horizontal axis and an interval of 2 on the vertical axis.

Step 3 For each elevation interval, draw a bar whose height is given by the frequency.

Exercises

For Exercises 1–3, use the information shown in the table below.

1. The frequency table shows voter participation in 2000. Display the data in a histogram.

Voter Participation by State (2000)

Percent voting	Tally	Frequency
35–39	I	1
40–44		0
45–49	卌 I	6
50–54	卌 卌 II	12
55–59	卌 卌 III	13
60–64	卌 卌 II	12
65–69	卌 I	6

Source: U.S. Census Bureau

Voter Participation by State (2000)

2. How many states had a voter turnout greater than 50 percent? **43**

3. How many states had fewer than 40 percent voting? **1**

Chapter 12   25   Glencoe Pre-Algebra

NAME _____ DATE _____ PERIOD _____

12-4 Lesson Reading Guide

Histograms

Get Ready for the Lesson

Read the introduction to Lesson 12-4 in your textbook. Write your answers below.

a. What does each tally mark represent? **a state**

b. What does the last column represent? **the totals in the row of tally marks**

c. What do you notice about the intervals that represent the counties?
They are equal.

Read the Lesson

Write a definition and give an example of the new vocabulary word.

Vocabulary	Definition	Example
1. histogram	**See students' work.**	

Complete the following statements about frequency tables and histograms.

2. If the first frequency interval goes from 1 to 50, the next frequency interval goes from **51–100** .

3. Because the intervals in a histogram are **equal** , all of the bars have the **same width** .

4. In a histogram, there is **no space between** bars.

5. Intervals that have a frequency of 0 have **no bar** .

6. The height of a bar in a histogram corresponds to the **frequency** of the data for that **interval** .

Remember What You Learned

7. Label the following in the histogram at right: interval, frequency, bar, and histogram. Then make a frequency table showing the same information as the histogram.

My Survey

Age	Tally	Frequency
0–19	卌 IIII	9
20–39	卌 I	6
40–59	卌 卌 I	11
60–79	III	3

Chapter 12   24   Glencoe Pre-Algebra

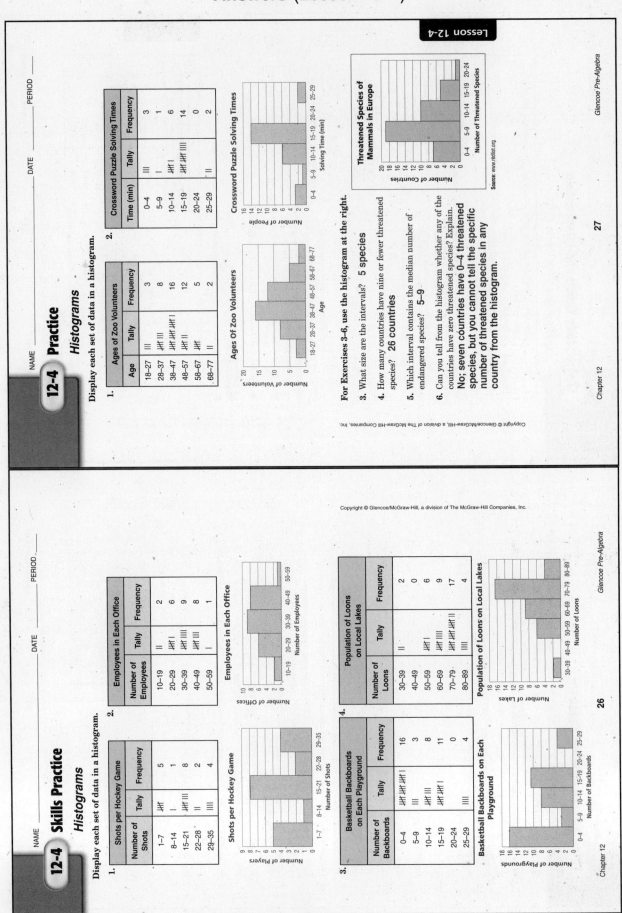

Skills Practice (page 26)

NAME _____ DATE _____ PERIOD _____

12-4 Skills Practice
Histograms

Display each set of data in a histogram.

1. Shots per Hockey Game

Number of Shots	Tally	Frequency
1–7	⁙	5
8–14	I	1
15–21	⁙ III	8
22–28	II	2
29–35	IIII	4

Shots per Hockey Game

2. Employees in Each Office

Number of Employees	Tally	Frequency
10–19	II	2
20–29	⁙ I	6
30–39	⁙ IIII	9
40–49	⁙ III	8
50–59	I	1

Employees in Each Office

3. Basketball Backboards on Each Playground

Number of Backboards	Tally	Frequency
0–4	⁙ ⁙ ⁙ I	16
5–9	III	3
10–14	⁙ III	8
15–19	⁙ ⁙ I	11
20–24		0
25–29	IIII	4

Basketball Backboards on Each Playground

4. Population of Loons on Local Lakes

Number of Loons	Tally	Frequency
30–39	II	2
40–49		0
50–59	⁙ I	6
60–69	⁙ IIII	9
70–79	⁙ ⁙ ⁙ II	17
80–89	IIII	4

Population of Loons on Local Lakes

Practice (page 27)

NAME _____ DATE _____ PERIOD _____

12-4 Practice
Histograms

Display each set of data in a histogram.

1. Ages of Zoo Volunteers

Age	Tally	Frequency
18–27	III	3
28–37	⁙ III	8
38–47	⁙ ⁙ ⁙ I	16
48–57	⁙ ⁙ II	12
58–67	⁙	5
68–77	II	2

Ages Of Zoo Volunteers

2. Crossword Puzzle Solving Times

Time (min)	Tally	Frequency
0–4	III	3
5–9	I	1
10–14	⁙ I	6
15–19	⁙ ⁙ IIII	14
20–24		0
25–29	II	2

Crossword Puzzle Solving Times

For Exercises 3–6, use the histogram at the right.

Threatened Species of Mammals in Europe

Source: www.redlist.org

3. What size are the intervals? **5 species**

4. How many countries have nine or fewer threatened species? **26 countries**

5. Which interval contains the median number of endangered species? **5–9**

6. Can you tell from the histogram whether any of the countries have zero threatened species? Explain. **No; seven countries have 0–4 threatened species, but you cannot tell the specific number of threatened species in any country from the histogram.**

Answers (Lesson 12-4)

NAME _____ DATE _____ PERIOD _____

12-4 Enrichment

Displaying Real-World Data

The Big D Marathon is an annual event that takes place in Dallas, Texas, in the spring. Marathons are 26.2 miles in length and require intense preparation and endurance. Here are the results from the 50-54 age group from the April 3, 2005, Big D Marathon. 3:58:08 means 3 hours, 58 minutes, 8 seconds.

Place	Name	Age	Time (hr:min:s)
1	Kathy Johnson	50	3:58:08
2	Lana Parks	51	4:17:16
3	Adrienne Gabriel	50	4:55:33
4	Sarah Gordon	50	5:07:45
5	Teresa Lynd	52	5:22:03
6	Margaret Darneille	53	5:25:56
7	Deborah Kerr-Leathem	51	5:34:36
8	Velena Cowsen	54	6:03:29
9	Kathy Davidson	50	6:15:50

Source: www.texasmarathon.com

1. Use the data to complete the frequency table below. Then draw a histogram to display the data. Number of Runners in Each Time Group

Time (in hours)	Tally	Frequency
3:00 - 3:59	I	1
4:00 - 4:59	II	2
5:00 - 5:59	IIII	4
6:00 - 6:59	II	2

2. Draw a stem-and-leaf plot to display the data for the times at which the runners completed the marathon.

Hours	Minutes
3	58
4	17 55
5	07 22 25 34
6	03 15

3 | 58 5 3:58

Finish Times for the Age Group (hr:min)

3. Draw a box-and-whiskers plot to display the times data.

4. What is the median time that this group of runners finished the marathon?

5:22:03

Chapter 12   29   Glencoe Pre-Algebra

NAME _____ DATE _____ PERIOD _____

12-4 Word Problem Practice

Histograms

1. **MUSIC** Students in grades 6-12 were asked, "Of the songs you listen to, what percent of the songs' lyrics do you know?" The histogram shows the results. How many students responded in all?

45 students

2. **VOLUNTEERING** The histogram shows how many hours per year a group of teens said they spend volunteering. How many hours did most of them volunteer?

between 20 and 39 hours/year

3. **MONEY** A group of students were asked. How much cash (in bills) is in your wallet right now? Construct a histogram to represent the data.

Amount	Number of Students
0-$9	54
$10-$19	20
$20-$29	16
$30-$39	5
$40-$49	4
$50-$59	1

4. **WEATHER** The list below shows the highest recorded temperature of the 20 largest U.S. cities. Display the data in a histogram.

122 110 111 106 109
105 104 104 105 102
104 106 102 104 108
112 113 109 111 103

Sample answer:

NEWSPAPERS For Exercises 5 and 6, use the histogram below.
Teens ages 13 to 18 who read a newspaper at least once a week were asked How many minutes a day, on average, do you spend reading the newspaper? The responses are displayed in the histogram.

5. How many teens said they read a newspaper for less than 30 minutes?

88 teens

6. How many teens were surveyed in all?

130 teens

Chapter 12   28   Glencoe Pre-Algebra

12-5 Lesson Reading Guide

NAME _____ DATE _____ PERIOD _____

Selecting an Appropriate Display

Get Ready for the Lesson

Read the introduction to Lesson 12-5 in your textbook. Write your answers below.

a. What type of graph can be used to display the data?
   Sample answer: line plot; See margin for graph.

b. Find another way to display the data that shows the number of items divided into specific categories. Draw the graph and describe how you named your categories.
   Sample answer: histogram; I divided the times into equal categories. See margin for graph.

c. Find a third way to display the data that shows how they are spread out. Draw the graph. **Sample answer: box-and-whisker plot. See margin for graph.**

Read the Lesson

Complete the following statements by filling in the blanks with the following words.

| circle graph | bar graph | box-and-whisker plot |
| frequency table | histogram | line graph |

1. The best time to use a __bar graph__ is when you would like to display the frequency of data using bars.

2. If you would like to compare the number of values in certain intervals, it is best to use a __frequency table__. If you would like to display this data, it is best to use a __histogram__.

3. If you would like to divide a set into four parts using the median and quartiles, a __box-and-whisker plot__ would be the best way to display the data.

4. To show changes over a period of time, you should display the data in a __line graph__.

5. To compare parts of data to the whole, you should display the data in a __circle graph__.

Remember What You Learned

6. Think of an example of a set of data you have seen in an earlier lesson. Explain what the benefits or drawbacks might be for using each of the possible data displays.
   See students' work.

Chapter 12   31   Glencoe Pre-Algebra

12-4 Spreadsheet Activity

NAME _____ DATE _____ PERIOD _____

Histograms

Example

Use a spreadsheet to make a histogram of the data on home runs.

Major League Baseball Home Runs in the 2001 Season

Team	Home Runs	Team	Home Runs	Team	Home Runs
Rangers	246	Dodgers	206	Braves	174	Royals	152
Giants	235	Yankees	203	Mariners	169	Mets	147
White Sox	214	Athletics	199	Marlins	166	Tigers	139
Rockies	213	Cardinals	199	Twins	164	Orioles	136
Indians	212	Red Sox	198	Phillies	164	Expos	131
Brewers	209	Blue Jays	195	Pirates	161	Devil Rays	121
Diamondbacks	208	Cubs	194	Padres	161		
Astros	208	Reds	176	Angels	158		

Source: MLB Advanced Media

Step 1 Enter the numbers of home runs into Column A. Enter the measurement classes into Column B. In this case, classes of 120, 130, 140, and so on, are appropriate.

Step 2 Choose Histogram from the Data Analysis menu on the Tools menu. Note that you may have to add this option if it is not already installed.

Step 3 In the Histogram dialog box, choose Column A for the Input Range and Column B for the Bin Range. Check the Chart Output box to have the computer sort the data and create the histogram. Click OK.

The spreadsheet will allow you to change the appearance of the graph by adding titles and axis labels, adjusting the scales on the axes, changing colors, and so on.

Exercises 1-2 See students' work.

1. Use a spreadsheet program to create a histogram of the home run data using measurement classes of 20.

2. Use the Internet or other reference to find some data on a subject of your choice. Create a histogram of the data.

Chapter 12   30   Glencoe Pre-Algebra

Answers (Lesson 12-5)

NAME _____ DATE _____ PERIOD _____

12-5 Study Guide and Intervention

Selecting an Appropriate Display

CHOOSE APPROPRIATE DISPLAYS Data can be visually represented in many different ways, including bar graphs, box-and-whisker plots, circle graphs, frequency tables, histograms, line graphs, line plots, stem-and-leaf plots, tables, and Venn diagrams.

Example HOUSING The table shows the total number of houses occupied in the U.S. from 1980–2003. Choose an appropriate type of display for this situation. Then make the display.

Year	1980	1985	1990	1995	2000	2001	2002	2003
Total Housing	79,638	87,887	94,224	99,985	105,720	107,010	104,965	105,560

The data can be represented in two ways. First, you can use a bar graph showing the number in each year. Second, you can use a line graph to show the change from 1980 to 2003.

Total U.S. Housing

Total U.S. Housing

Exercise

Choose an appropriate type of display for the data set. Then make the display.

See students' work.

Player	Points Per Game
Allen Iverson	33.2
LeBron James	30.7
Gilbert Arenas	29.1
Dwyane Wade	27.7
Paul Pierce	27.1

Source: espn.com

Chapter 12   32   Glencoe Pre-Algebra

NAME _____ DATE _____ PERIOD _____

12-5 Skills Practice

Selecting an Appropriate Display

Choose an appropriate style of display for each data set. Justify your choice.

1. the life span of various types of fish
   stem-and-leaf plot; lists all the data in a condensed form

2. the number of teachers for 5 different high schools
   bar graph; displays the frequency of data using bars

3. the number of students who are in a band, science club, and/or student council
   Venn diagram; shows a relationship between the three groups of people

4. the names of the Nobel prize winners for the past 50 years
   table; lists data individually

5. the total rainfall for several 100-day time intervals
   histogram; displays data that has been organized into equal time intervals

6. **PARTY** A class of 26 students voted on which type of snack they would like to have at their class party. 13 students voted for brownies, 7 voted for ice cream, 5 voted for cookies, and 2 voted for pretzels. Which graph best represents this situaton? **D**

   A. Snack Preference Votes

   0 1 2 3 4 5 6 7 8 9 10 11 12 13 14

   B.

Snack	Frequency
Brownies	IIII IIII III
Ice Cream	IIII II
Cookies	IIII
Pretzels	II

   C. Snack Preference

   D. Snack Preference

   Pretzels 8%
   Cookies 20%
   Brownies 27%
   Ice Cream 50%

Chapter 12   33   Glencoe Pre-Algebra

Answers (Lesson 12-5)

Chapter 12

Page 34 (left)

12-5 Practice

Selecting an Appropriate Display

Choose an appropriate style of display for each data set. Justify your choice.

1. the monthly price of apples over a two year period.
line graph; shows change over period of time

2. results of a poll of 30 students favorite type of candy
circle graph; compares parts of data to the whole

3. the income of the middle 50% of U.S. households
box-and-whisker plot; divides the data by the median and quartiles

4. the number of terms served by current senators
stem-and-leaf plot, lists all the data in a condensed form

5. the number of runners who finished a marathon in each ten-minute interval
frequency table; compares the number of values in each interval

Choose an appropriate style of display for each data set. Then make a display.

6. Winning times for the 200-Meter backstroke event at the Olympics.

See students' work.

Year	Winning Time
1976	1:59.19
1980	2:01.93
1984	2:00.23
1988	1:59.37
1992	1:58.47
1996	1:58.54
2000	1:56.76
2004	1:54.95

Source: World Almanac

7.

Monthly Park Visitors (in thousands)	
6	12
15	40
46	37
22	8
6	7
15	25
46	46
22	19

See students' work.

Page 35 (right)

12-5 Word Problem Practice

Selecting an Appropriate Display

1. **RADIO** The table below shows the average amount of time that teenagers spent listening to the radio from 1999 to 2003. What would be an appropriate way to display the data?

Year	1999	2000	2001	2002	2003
Hours/week	11.4	10.5	10.0	9.25	8.5

line graph or bar graph

2. **TELEVISION** The table below shows the number of hours students spend watching TV in one week. What would be an appropriate way to display the data?

Students	1-10	11-20	21-30	31-40	40+
Hours	6	19	14	4	1

histogram

3. **ENTERTAINMENT** Teens spend more time on the Internet than with any other form of media. In an average week, they spend 16.7 hours online versus 13.6 hours watching TV, and 12 hours listening to the radio. Display the data using the most appropriate display.

Sample answer: circle graph

39.5% Online
32.1% TV
28.4% Radio

4. **MONEY MATTERS** The table below shows the minimum age that a person must be in order to obtain a full driver's license. Would a box-and-whisker plot be an appropriate display of the data set? Explain.

State	CT	GA	ID	NJ	TX
Minimum age (yr, mo)	16, 6	18,0	15,0	17,0	16,0

Source: http://gokcalnet.com/drivingage/

Sample answer: No; a box-and-whisker plot requires data that are divided into four parts. This data set only has five values.

VIDEO GAMES For Exercises 5-7, use the information below.

The table shows some of the recent top selling video game categories.

Genre	Percent
Action	30.1%
Children	9.5%
Racing	9.4%
Simulation	9.0%
Sports	17.8%

Source: www.theesa.com/archives

5. What type of graph would best represents the data if each category is to be compared to the whole?
circle graph

6. What type of graph would best represents the data if the categories are to be compared to each other?
bar graph

7. Suppose you wanted to compare how the percent of action games had changed over the last 5 years. What type of graph would best represent the situation?
line graph

Answers (Lessons 12-5 and 12-6)

12-5 Enrichment

NAME _____ DATE _____ PERIOD _____

Statistical Graphs

Bar graphs and pictographs are used to compare quantities. Line graphs are used to show changes. Circle graphs compare parts to parts, or parts to the whole.

Solve. Use the pictograph.

Principal Languages of the World
(to nearest fifty million)

English	☺☺☺☺
Hindi	☺☺↷
Arabic	☺↷
Portuguese	☺↷
Chinese	☺☺☺☺☺☺☺
Russian	☺☺↷
Spanish	☺☺☺
French	☺
Bengali	☺↷

☺ = 100 million

1. How many people speak Portuguese?
   150,000,000

2. What is the ratio of people who speak Spanish to those who speak Russian?
   1:1

3. What three languages are each spoken by about 150 million people? Arabic, Portuguese, Bengali

4. How many fewer people speak Arabic than Hindi? 100,000,000

Solve. Use the circle graph.

5. Which continent has the smallest population? Australia

6. How does the population of South America compare to that of Africa?
   South America has about half as many people.

7. What is the population of Australia if the world's population is about 6 billion?
   about 18,000,000

Population by Continent: Asia 59.7%, Europe 15.1%, North Am. 8.3%, South Am. 5.5%, Africa 10.9%, Australia 0.3%

Solve. Use the line graph.

Price Received by Farmers for One Dozen Eggs

8. During which ten-year period was the increase in the price of eggs greatest?
   1940–1950

9. What was the price of a dozen eggs in 1940? 16¢

10. What was the percent of increase in the price of eggs from 1940 to 1950?
    about 120–140%

11. What was the increase in cents from 1930 to 1980? about 32¢

Chapter 12   36   Glencoe Pre-Algebra

12-6 Lesson Reading Guide

NAME _____ DATE _____ PERIOD _____

Misleading Graphs

Get Ready for the Lesson

Read the introduction to Lesson 12-6 in your textbook. Write your answers below.

a. Do both graphs show the same information? yes

b. Which graph suggests a dramatic increase in sales from May to June?
   Graph B

c. Which graph suggests steady sales? Graph A

d. How are the graphs similar? How are they different? Sample answer: The graphs differ in that Graph A shows a gradual increase and decrease over the year; Graph B shows a drastic increase and decrease. They are similar in that each graph contains labeled axes and a title.

Reading the Lesson

Complete the following statements by filling in the blanks with the following words.

different   gradually   horizontal   interval(s)
label(s)   rapidly   title(s)   vertical

1. If two graphs showing the same information have different vertical scales, that means that on the vertical axis, the intervals are different.

2. If two graphs showing the same information have different horizontal scales, that means that on the horizontal axis, the intervals are different.

3. A graph can be misleading if it has no title or if it has no labels on the scales.

4. If a graph shows steady change, the plotted values should increase or decrease gradually.

5. If a graph shows dramatic change, the plotted values should increase or decrease rapidly.

Remember What You Learned

6. Use a dictionary and a book of synonyms to rewrite the following sentence by replacing the underlined words with ones you are more familiar with.
   Statistics or statistical graphs can be misleading when the same data are represented in different ways, so that each graph gives a different visual impression.
   Sample answer: A collection of numerical information or statistical graphs can be deceptive when the same facts are shown in different ways, so that each graph gives a different effect to the eyes.

Chapter 12   37   Glencoe Pre-Algebra

Lesson 12-6

Study Guide and Intervention (Lesson 12-6)

12-6 Study Guide and Intervention
Misleading Graphs

Example The graphs below show the increase in the number of events held in the Summer Olympics from 1948 to 1996.

Events in Summer Olympics
Graph A

Events in Summer Olympics
Graph B

a. What causes the graphs to differ in their appearance?

Different vertical scales and the lack of a zero on Graph A's axis result in different visual impressions.

b. Which graph appears to show a more rapid increase in the number of events held in the Summer Olympics? Explain.

Graph A; the steeper slope of the line and the higher position of the line relative to the scale make it appear that the number of events is greater and increasing faster.

Exercises

For Exercises 1–3, refer to the graphs below.

Highest Temperatures
Graph A

Highest Temperatures
Graph B

Source: National Oceanic and Atmospheric Administration

1. What is the highest recorded temperature in California? In Alaska? **134°F; 100°F**

2. In which graph does the difference between these two temperatures appear to be minimized? **Graph B**

3. How do the graphs create different appearances? **The vertical scale on Graph A has a smaller range than the scale on Graph B.**

Chapter 12   38   *Glencoe Pre-Algebra*

Skills Practice (Lesson 12-6)

12-6 Skills Practice
Misleading Graphs

For Exercises 1–3, refer to the graphs below.

Most Common Lake Names
in Wisconsin
Graph A

Most Common Lake Names
in Wisconsin
Graph B

Source: Wisconsin Department of Natural Resources

1. How many lakes in Wisconsin are named Bass Lake? Long Lake? Mud Lake? **82; 59; 116**

2. Which graph gives the impression that only a few lakes are called Long Lake, while numerous lakes are called Bass Lake? **Graph A**

3. What causes the graphs to differ in their appearance? **The vertical axis of Graph A starts at 55 instead of zero. This makes it appear that the name Long Lake is used much less frequently than Bass Lake.**

For Exercises 4–6, refer to the graphs below.

U.S. Corn Production, 1991–2001
Graph A

U.S. Corn Production, 1991–2001
Graph B

Source: USDA

4. Do these graphs show the same information? **yes**

5. Which graph suggests that U.S. corn production is relatively stable? **Graph B**

6. What causes the graphs to differ in their appearance? **The vertical scales are different. Graph A runs from 6 billion bushels to 11 billion bushels, while Graph B runs from 0 to 15 billion bushels.**

Chapter 12   39   *Glencoe Pre-Algebra*

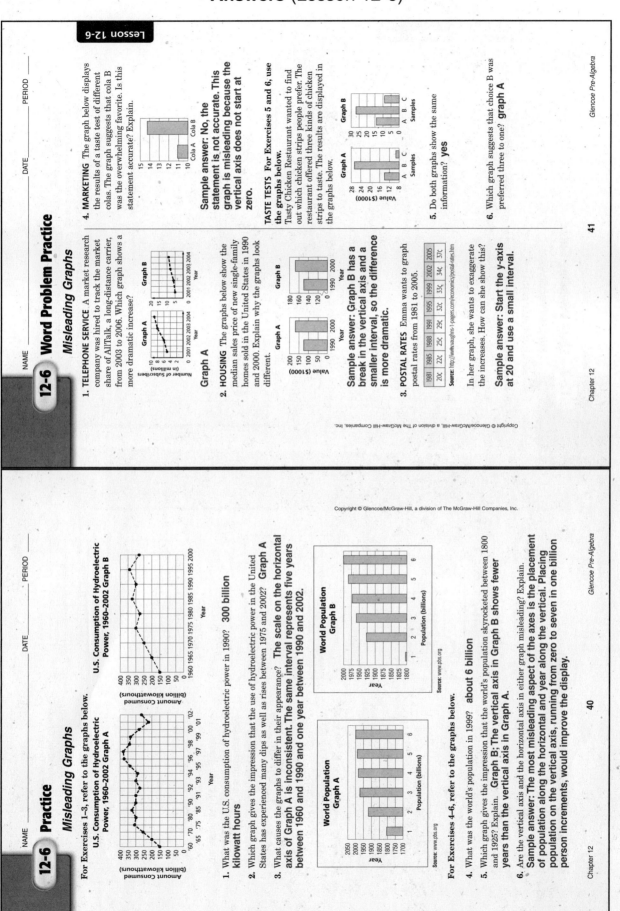

Lesson 12-6

NAME _____ DATE _____ PERIOD _____

12-6 Word Problem Practice
Misleading Graphs

1. TELEPHONE SERVICE A market research company was hired to track the market share of AllTalk, a long-distance carrier, from 2003 to 2006. Which graph shows a more dramatic increase?

Graph A

Graph B

Graph A

2. HOUSING The graphs below show the median sales price of new single-family homes sold in the United States in 1990 and 2000. Explain why the graphs look different.

Graph A   Graph B

Sample answer: Graph B has a break in the vertical axis and a smaller interval, so the difference is more dramatic.

3. POSTAL RATES Emma wants to graph postal rates from 1981 to 2005.

1981	1985	1988	1991	1995	1999	2002	2005
20¢	22¢	25¢	29¢	32¢	33¢	34¢	37¢

Source: http://www.aughter-1-papers.com/economics/postal-rates.htm

In her graph, she wants to exaggerate the increases. How can she show this?

Sample answer: Start the y-axis at 20 and use a small interval.

4. MARKETING The graph below displays the results of a taste test of different colas. The graph suggests that cola B was the overwhelming favorite. Is this statement accurate? Explain.

Cola A   Cola B

Sample answer: No, the statement is not accurate. This graph is misleading because the vertical axis does not start at zero.

TASTE TESTS For Exercises 5 and 6, use the graphs below.
Tasty Chicken Restaurant wanted to find out which chicken strips people prefer. The restaurant offered three kinds of chicken strips to taste. The results are displayed in the graphs below.

Graph A   Graph B

5. Do both graphs show the same information? **yes**

6. Which graph suggests that choice B was preferred three to one? **graph A**

Chapter 12   41   Glencoe Pre-Algebra

NAME _____ DATE _____ PERIOD _____

12-6 Practice
Misleading Graphs

For Exercises 1–3, refer to the graphs below.

U.S. Consumption of Hydroelectric Power, 1960–2002 Graph A

U.S. Consumption of Hydroelectric Power, 1960–2002 Graph B

1. What was the U.S. consumption of hydroelectric power in 1990? **300 billion kilowatt hours**

2. Which graph gives the impression that the use of hydroelectric power in the United States has experienced many dips as well as rises between 1975 and 2002? **Graph A**

3. What causes the graphs to differ in their appearance? **The scale on the horizontal axis of Graph A is inconsistent. The same interval represents five years between 1960 and 1990 and one year between 1990 and 2002.**

For Exercises 4–6, refer to the graphs below.

World Population Graph A

Source: www.pbs.org

World Population Graph B

Source: www.pbs.org

4. What was the world's population in 1999? **about 6 billion**

5. Which graph gives the impression that the world's population skyrocketed between 1800 and 1925? Explain. **Graph B; The vertical axis in Graph B shows fewer years than the vertical axis in Graph A.**

6. Are the vertical axis and the horizontal axis in either graph misleading? Explain. **Sample answer: The most misleading aspect of the axes is the placement of population along the horizontal and year along the vertical. Placing population on the vertical axis, running from zero to seven in one billion person increments, would improve the display.**

Chapter 12   40   Glencoe Pre-Algebra

Answers (Lessons 12-6 and 12-7)

12-7 Lesson Reading Guide

Simple Probability

Get Ready for the Lesson

Read the introduction to Lesson 12-7 in your textbook. Write your answers below.

a. Write the ratio that compares the number of tiles labeled E to the total number of tiles. $\dfrac{12}{100}$

b. What percent of the tiles are labeled E? **12%**

c. What fraction of tiles is this? $\dfrac{3}{25}$

d. Suppose a player chooses a tile. Is there a better chance of choosing a D or an N? Explain. **There is a better chance of choosing an N because there are more of them.**

Read the Lesson 1–6. **See students' work.**

Write a definition and give an example of each new vocabulary word or phrase.

Vocabulary	Definition	Example
1. outcomes		
2. simple event		
3. probability		
4. sample space		
5. theoretical probability		
6. experimental probability		

Remember What You Learned

7. Look up *theoretical* and *experimental* in the dictionary. How can their definitions help you remember the difference between theoretical probability and experimental probability? **Theoretical means based on theory or speculation; theoretical probability is what *should* occur. Experimental means based on experience or experiment; experimental probability is what *actually* occurs.**

12-6 Enrichment

Using and Misusing Graphs

Refer to the graphs at the right.

1. Do Graphs A and B give the same information on sales? **yes**

2. Find the ratio of Hilly's sales to Valley's sales. **3:1**

3. In Graph A, the Hilly van is about 2.5 cm high by 6 cm long. What is its area? **15 cm²**

4. The Valley van is about 0.75 cm high by 2 cm long. What is its area? **1.5 cm²**

5. In Graph B, both vans are about 1.5 cm high. The Hilly van is about 6 cm long. What is its area? **9 cm²**

6. The Valley van is about 2 cm long. What is its area? **3 cm²**

7. Compute the following ratios.

   Graph A: $\dfrac{\text{Area of Hilly}}{\text{Area of Valley}}$ $\dfrac{10}{1}$

   Graph B: $\dfrac{\text{Area of Hilly}}{\text{Area of Valley}}$ $\dfrac{3}{1}$

8. Compare the results of Exercises 2 and 7. Which graph is misleading? Explain your answer. **A; The actual number of vans sold by Hilly's is 3 times greater, but Graph A appears to show the sales as 10 times greater.**

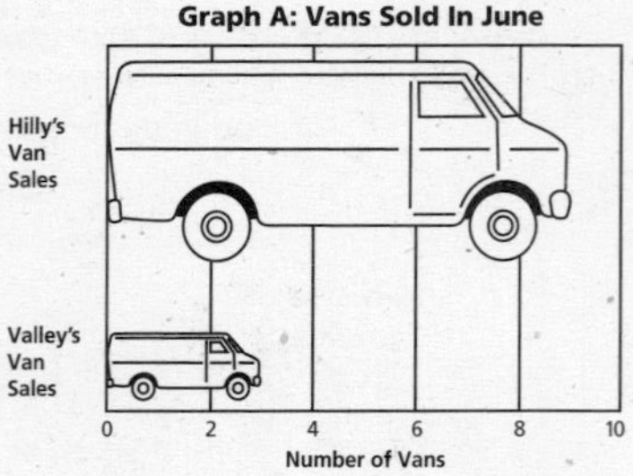

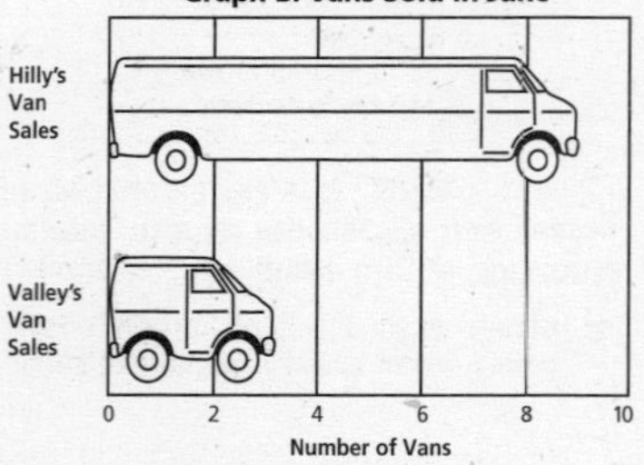

Use Graphs C and D to answer each question.

9. Which graph is easier to read? **C**

10. Compare the vertical scales. How do they differ? **The units on Graph C increase by 1, while the units on Graph D increase by 10.**

11. Which graph gives a better impression of the trend in sales? Explain. **Sample answer: Neither; the sales increase is overstated by Graph C and understated by Graph D.**

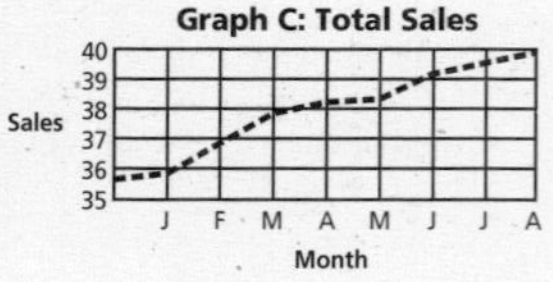

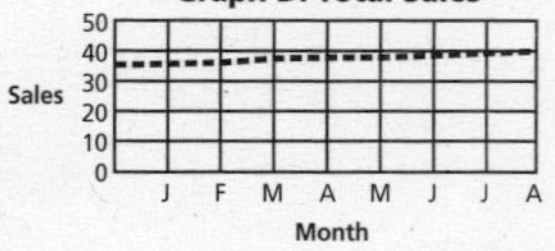

Graph A: Vans Sold In June

Graph B: Vans Sold In June

Graph C: Total Sales

Graph D: Total Sales

Answers (Lesson 12-7)

12-7 Skills Practice
Simple Probability

A spinner like the one shown is used in a game. Determine the probability of each outcome if the spinner is equally likely to land on each section. Express each probability as a fraction and as a percent.

1. $P(10)$ $\frac{1}{16}$, 6.25%
2. $P(\text{odd})$ $\frac{1}{2}$, 50%
3. $P(\text{greater than 7})$ $\frac{9}{16}$, 56.25%
4. $P(\text{prime})$ $\frac{3}{8}$, 37.5%
5. $P(\text{1 or 2})$ $\frac{1}{8}$, 12.5%
6. $P(\text{less than 5})$ $\frac{1}{4}$, 25%
7. $P(\text{Shaded})$ $\frac{5}{16}$, 31.25%
8. $P(\text{Not shaded})$ $\frac{11}{16}$, 68.75%

There are 4 red marbles, 1 blue marble, 9 green marbles, and 6 yellow marble in a bag. Suppose one marble is selected at random. Find the probability of each outcome. Express each probability as a fraction and as a percent.

9. $P(\text{red})$ $\frac{1}{5}$, 20%
10. $P(\text{blue})$ $\frac{1}{20}$, 5%
11. $P(\text{yellow})$ $\frac{3}{10}$, 30%
12. $P(\text{red or blue})$ $\frac{1}{4}$, 25%
13. $P(\text{white})$ $\frac{0}{1}$, 0%
14. $P(\text{red, blue, or green})$ $\frac{7}{10}$, 70%

Suppose two 1–6 number cubes are rolled. Find the probability of each outcome. Express each probability as a fraction and as a percent. (*Hint:* Make a table to show the sample space as in Example 2.) Round to the nearest tenth, if necessary.

15. $P(\text{3 or 5})$ $\frac{5}{9}$, 55.6%
16. $P(\text{both even})$ $\frac{1}{4}$, 25%
17. $P(\text{odd product})$ $\frac{1}{4}$, 25%
18. $P(\text{sum more than 10})$ $\frac{1}{12}$, 8.3%
19. $P(\text{both the same})$ $\frac{1}{6}$, 16.7%
20. $P(\text{product is a square})$ $\frac{2}{9}$, 22.2%

12-7 Study Guide and Intervention
Simple Probability

Probability is the chance some event will happen.

$$P(\text{event}) = \frac{\text{number of favorable outcomes}}{\text{number of possible outcomes}}$$

Example A bag contains 6 red marbles, 1 blue marble, and 3 yellow marbles. One marble is selected at random. Find the probability of each outcome.

a. P(yellow)
$$P(\text{event}) = \frac{\text{number of favorable outcomes}}{\text{number of possible outcomes}}$$
$$= \frac{3}{10} \text{ or } 30\%$$
There is a 30% chance of choosing a yellow marble.

b. P(blue or yellow)
$$P(\text{event}) = \frac{\text{number of favorable outcomes}}{\text{number of possible outcomes}}$$
$$= \frac{(1+3)}{10} = \frac{4}{10} \text{ or } 40\%$$
There is a 40% chance of choosing a blue or yellow marble.

c. P(red, blue, or yellow)
$$P(\text{event}) = \frac{\text{number of favorable outcomes}}{\text{number of possible outcomes}}$$
$$= \frac{(6+1+3)}{10} = \frac{10}{10} \text{ or } 100\%$$
There is a 100% chance of choosing a red, blue, or yellow marble.

d. P(black)
$$P(\text{event}) = \frac{\text{number of favorable outcomes}}{\text{number of possible outcomes}}$$
$$= \frac{0}{10} \text{ or } 0\%$$
There is a 0% chance of choosing a black marble.

Exercises
A bag contains 5 red marbles, 5 blue marbles, 6 green marbles, 8 purple marbles, and 1 white marble. One is selected at random. Find the probability of each outcome. Express each probability as a fraction and as a percent.

1. $P(\text{white})$ $\frac{1}{25}$, 4%
2. $P(\text{red})$ $\frac{1}{5}$, 20%
3. $P(\text{green})$ $\frac{6}{25}$, 24%
4. $P(\text{purple})$ $\frac{8}{25}$, 32%
5. $P(\text{white, blue, or green})$ $\frac{12}{25}$, 48%
6. $P(\text{red or blue})$ $\frac{2}{5}$, 40%
7. $P(\text{red or purple})$ $\frac{13}{25}$, 52%
8. $P(\text{green or purple})$ $\frac{14}{25}$, 56%
9. $P(\text{green, purple, or white})$ $\frac{3}{5}$, 60%
10. $P(\text{red, blue, green, purple, or white})$ $\frac{1}{1}$, 100%
11. $P(\text{red, blue, or purple})$ $\frac{18}{25}$, 72%

Answers (Lesson 12-7)

12-7 Practice

Simple Probability

NAME _____ DATE _____ PERIOD _____

A spinner like the one shown is used in a game. Determine the probability of each outcome if the spinner is equally likely to land on each section. Express each probability as a fraction and as a percent.

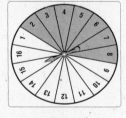

1. $P(15)$

$\dfrac{1}{16}$, 6.25%

2. $P(\text{even})$

$\dfrac{1}{2}$, 50%

3. $P(\text{greater than }10)$

$\dfrac{3}{8}$, 37.5

4. $P(\text{perfect square})$

$\dfrac{1}{4}$, 25%

5. $P(1 \text{ or } 2)$

$\dfrac{1}{8}$, 12.5%

6. $P(\text{less than }9)$

$\dfrac{1}{2}$, 50%

7. $P(\text{not shaded})$

$\dfrac{9}{16}$, 56.25%

8. $P(\text{shaded})$

$\dfrac{7}{16}$, 43.75%

There are 8 red marbles, 5 blue marbles, 11 green marbles, and 1 yellow marble in a bag. Suppose one marble is selected at random. Find the probability of each outcome. Express each probability as a fraction and as a percent.

9. $P(\text{red})$

$\dfrac{8}{25}$, 32%

10. $P(\text{blue})$

$\dfrac{1}{5}$, 20%

11. $P(\text{yellow})$

$\dfrac{1}{25}$, 4%

12. $P(\text{red or blue})$

$\dfrac{13}{25}$, 52%

13. $P(\text{black})$

$\dfrac{0}{1}$, 0%

14. $P(\text{red, blue, or green})$

$\dfrac{24}{25}$, 96%

Suppose two 1–6 number cubes are rolled. Find the probability of each outcome. Express each probability as a fraction and as a percent. (Hint: Make a table to show the sample space as in Example 2.) Round to the nearest tenth if necessary.

15. $P(1 \text{ or } 5)$

$\dfrac{5}{9}$, 55.6%

16. $P(\text{both odd})$

$\dfrac{1}{4}$, 25%

17. $P(\text{even product})$

$\dfrac{3}{4}$, 75%

18. $P(\text{sum more than }8)$

$\dfrac{5}{18}$, 27.8%

19. $P(\text{both different})$

$\dfrac{5}{6}$, 83.3%

20. $P(\text{sum is a square})$

$\dfrac{7}{36}$, 19.4%

21. To the nearest tenth of a percent, what is the probability that today is a weekday?
71.4%

12-7 Word Problem Practice

Simple Probability

NAME _____ DATE _____ PERIOD _____

1. **PINS AND NEEDLES** A pin is dropped at random onto the rectangle below. The pin lands in one of the small squares. What is the probability that the pin lands inside a gray square?

$\dfrac{9}{24}$ or 0.375

2. **VIDEO GAMES** Tyler has 14 video games. Five are action/adventure games, 2 are arcade games, 1 is a racing game, and 6 are sports games. Tyler cannot decide which game to play, so he will choose one without looking. What is the probability that the game he chooses is an arcade game?

$\dfrac{1}{7}$ or about 0.14

3. **VOLUNTEERING** Aisha surveyed her classmates to find out where they get their news. Of a group of 320 teens, about how many get their news online?

Where Teens Get Their News

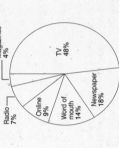

Magazines 4%

Radio 7%

Online 9%

Word of mouth 14%

TV 48%

Newspaper 18%

Source: usaweekend.com

about 29

4. **CANDY** A bag of chewy candies contains 22 cherry, 16 green apple, 15 lemonade, 15 orange, and 9 grape candies. Lashanda picks a piece from the bag without looking. What is the probability that she will pick a grape candy? Express the answer as a decimal rounded to the nearest hundredth and as a percent. **0.12; 12%**

FUND-RAISING For Exercises 5–7, use the following information.
To raise money, Angie's class sold 80 boxes of cookies. She made the table below to show which cookies they sold the most.

Bestselling Baker Cookies	
Mints Cookies	25%
Caramel Cookies	19%
Peanut Butter Cookies	13%
Chocolate Cookies	11%
Butter Cookies	9%

5. About how many people bought chocolate cookies? **about 9 people**

6. About how many people bought caramel cookies? **about 15 people**

7. How many people would you expect to say that they bought another type of Baker Cookie that is not listed in the table? **about 18 people**

Answers (Lessons 12-7 and 12-8)

12-7 Enrichment

Probability and Tables

SCHOOL In Rockville High School there are

400 freshmen—60 have A averages and 90 have B averages.
300 sophomores—40 have A averages and 60 have B averages.
200 juniors—10 have A averages and 30 have B averages.
100 seniors—20 have A averages and 60 have B averages.

1. Use the information above to complete the table below. Then use the table to answer Exercises 2–11.

Class	Grade A	B	Below B	Total
Freshmen	60	90	250	400
Sophomores	40	60	200	300
Juniors	10	30	160	200
Seniors	20	60	20	100
Total	130	240	630	1000

Suppose a student is selected at random from Rockville High School. Find the probability of selecting each of the following.

2. a freshman $\frac{2}{5}$ or 40%

3. a senior $\frac{1}{10}$ or 10%

4. an A student $\frac{13}{100}$ or 13%

5. a student whose grade is below B $\frac{63}{100}$ or 63%

6. a sophomore B student $\frac{3}{50}$ or 6%

7. a junior A student or a senior A student $\frac{3}{100}$ or 3%

8. a student who is neither a junior A student nor a senior A student $\frac{97}{100}$ or 97%

9. a B student who is *not* a junior $\frac{21}{100}$ or 21%

10. If selecting only from the juniors, what is the probability of picking an A student? $\frac{1}{20}$ or 5%

11. If selecting only from the students who are neither A nor B students, what is the probability of picking a senior? $\frac{2}{63}$ or about 3.2%

Chapter 12
48
Glencoe Pre-Algebra

12-8 Lesson Reading Guide

Counting Outcomes

Get Ready for the Lesson

Read the introduction to Lesson 12-8 in your textbook. Write your answers below.

a. Write the names of each deck choice on 5 sticky notes of one color. Write the names of each type of wheel on 3 notes of another color. **See students' work.**

b. Choose one deck note and one wheel note. One possible skateboard is Alien, Eagle. **See students' work.**

c. Make a list of all the possible skateboards. alien-eagle, alien-cloud, alien-red hot, birdman-eagle, birdman-cloud, birdman-red hot, candy-eagle, candy-cloud, candy-red hot, radical-eagle, radical-cloud, radical-red hot, trickster-eagle, trickster-cloud, trickster-red hot

d. How many different skateboard designs are possible? 15

Read the Lesson 1–2. See students' work.

Write a definition and give an example of each new vocabulary phrase.

Vocabulary	Definition	Example
1. tree diagram		
2. Fundamental Counting Principle		

Remember What You Learned

3. Complete the two diagrams below by filling in each blank with one of the following words. Some words may be used more than once.

choices
favorable
outcomes
possible

Fundamental Counting Principle: m choices for event 1 $\times$ n choices for event 2 $=$ number of possible outcomes

Probability $=$ $\dfrac{\text{number of favorable outcomes}}{\text{number of possible outcomes}}$

Chapter 12
49
Glencoe Pre-Algebra

Lesson 12-8

Copyright © Glencoe/McGraw-Hill, a division of The McGraw-Hill Companies, Inc.

Chapter 12

A23

Glencoe Pre-Algebra

Answers (Lesson 12-8)

12-8 Skills Practice

Counting Outcomes

Draw a tree diagram to find the number of outcomes for each situation.

1. Three coins are tossed.

Coin 1	Coin 2	Coin 3	Outcomes
H	H	H	HHH
		T	HHT
	T	H	HTH
		T	HTT
T	H	H	THH
		T	THT
	T	H	TTH
		T	TTT

2. A number cube is rolled and a coin is tossed.

Number Cube	Coin	Outcomes
1	Heads	1, Heads
1	Tails	1, Tails
2	Heads	2, Heads
2	Tails	2, Tails
3	Heads	3, Heads
3	Tails	3, Tails
4	Heads	4, Heads
4	Tails	4, Tails
5	Heads	5, Heads
5	Tails	5, Tails
6	Heads	6, Heads
6	Tails	6, Tails

Find the number of possible outcomes for each situation.

3. One card is drawn from a standard deck of cards. **52 outcomes**

4. Three six-sided number cubes are rolled. **216 outcomes**

5. One coin is flipped three consecutive times. **8 outcomes**

6. One coin is flipped and one eight-sided die is rolled. **16 outcomes**

7. A sweater comes in 3 sizes and 6 colors. **18 outcomes**

8. A restaurant offers dinners with a choice each of two salads, six entrees, and five desserts. **60 outcomes**

Find the probability of each event.

9. Draw the ace of spades from a standard deck of cards. $\frac{1}{52}$

10. A coin is tossed twice. What is the probability of getting two tails? $\frac{1}{4}$

11. Draw the six of clubs from a standard deck of cards. $\frac{1}{52}$

12. Roll a 4 or higher on a six-sided number cube. $\frac{1}{2}$

13. Roll a 7 or an 8 on an eight-sided die. $\frac{1}{4}$

14. Roll an even number on an eight-sided die. $\frac{1}{2}$

15. Draw a club from a standard deck of cards. $\frac{1}{4}$

16. Roll an odd number on a six-sided number cube. $\frac{1}{2}$

17. A coin is tossed and an eight-sided die is rolled. What is the probability that the coin lands on tails, and the die lands on a 2? $\frac{1}{16}$

18. A coin is tossed and a card is drawn from a standard deck of cards. What is the probability of landing on tails and choosing a red card? $\frac{1}{4}$

12-8 Study Guide and Intervention

Counting Outcomes

Example 1 How many different combinations of beverage and bread can be made from 3 beverage choices and 3 bread choices?

Draw a tree diagram to find the number of different combinations.

List each beverage choice.

Each beverage choice is paired with each bread choice.

Beverage	Bread	Outcome
Coffee	Bagel	Coffee, Bagel
	Muffin	Coffee, Muffin
	Scone	Coffee, Scone
Tea	Bagel	Tea, Bagel
	Muffin	Tea, Muffin
	Scone	Tea, Scone
Juice	Bagel	Juice, Bagel
	Muffin	Juice, Muffin
	Scone	Juice, Scone

There are 9 possible outcomes.

The **Fundamental Counting Principle** also relates the number of outcomes to the number of choices. When you know the number of outcomes, you can find the probability that an event will occur.

Example 2 Refer to Example 1. What is the probability of randomly selecting coffee with a scone?

Use the Fundamental Counting Principle to find the number of outcomes.

$$\underset{\substack{\text{beverage}\\\text{choices}}}{3} \quad \underset{\text{times}}{\times} \quad \underset{\substack{\text{bread}\\\text{choices}}}{3} \quad \underset{\text{equals}}{=} \quad \underset{\substack{\text{total number}\\\text{of possible}\\\text{outcomes}}}{9}$$

Only one of the 9 possible outcomes is coffee and a scone.

So, the probability of randomly selecting coffee with a scone is $\frac{1}{9}$.

Exercises

Find the number of possible outcomes for each situation.

1. one six-sided number cube is rolled, and one card is drawn from a 52-card deck **312**

2. There are 512 juniors and 498 seniors. One junior and one senior are randomly drawn as raffle winners. **254,976**

Find the probability of each event.

3. A coin is tossed and a card is drawn from a 52-card deck. What is the probability of getting tails and the ten of diamonds? $\frac{1}{104}$

4. Four coins are tossed. What is the probability of four tails? $\frac{1}{16}$

Answers (Lesson 12-8)

NAME _____ DATE _____ PERIOD _____

12-8 Practice

Counting Outcomes

Find the number of possible outcomes for each situation.

1. Joan randomly dials a seven-digit phone number. **10,000,000 outcomes**

2. First-year students at a school must choose one each of 5 English classes, 4 history classes, 5 math classes, and 3 physical education classes. **300 outcomes**

3. One card each is drawn from four different standard decks of cards. **7,311,616 outcomes**

4. A store offers running shoes with either extra stability or extra cushioning from four different manufacturers. **8 outcomes**

5. A winter sweater comes in wool or fleece, with a zipper or a crew neck, and in three colors. **12 outcomes**

6. One spinner can land on red, green, blue, or yellow and another can land on right foot, left foot, right hand, or left hand. Each spinner is spun once. **16 outcomes**

Find the probability of each event.

7. A number cube is rolled. What is the probability of rolling a 4 or lower? $\dfrac{2}{3}$

8. A number cube is rolled. What is the probability of getting a five or higher? $\dfrac{1}{3}$

9. An eight-sided die is rolled and a coin is tossed. What is the probability of landing on an even number and getting heads? $\dfrac{1}{4}$

10. A coin is tossed and a card is drawn from a standard deck of cards. What is the probability of landing on heads and choosing a heart? $\dfrac{1}{8}$

11. **REFRESHMENTS** How many fruit smoothies are possible from 6 choices of fruit, 4 choices of milk, and 3 sizes? **72 fruit smoothies**

12. **MONOGRAMS** A school's class rings can include a student's initials in an engraved monogram on the ring. How many different monograms are possible from 2 sizes, 5 type styles, and 3 border styles? **30 monograms**

13. **MOBILE PHONES** The table shows the features you can choose for a pay-as-you go phone plan.

Phone	Features	Calling Area	Monthly Talk Time
Brand A; Brand B	e-mail only; paging only; deluxe: paging and e-mail	local only; local and regional; national long distance	30 min; 60 min; 100 min

   a. How many phone plans have national long distance? **18 plans**

   b. How many customized phone plans include 100 minutes per month talkingtime and paging capabilities? **12 plans**

NAME _____ DATE _____ PERIOD _____

12-8 Word Problem Practice

Counting Outcomes

1. **SPORTS** Khalil plays on the interleague soccer team at school. The team has practice jerseys for the players. The jerseys come in blue, black, or gray, in sizes small, medium, and large. Draw a tree diagram to list all of the practice jerseys Khalil can choose from.

2. **CLOTHING** Brittany is choosing an outfit to wear to the football game on Friday night. She has 5 sweaters, 7 turtlenecks, and 8 pairs of pants from which to choose. How many different outfits can she choose from? **280**

3. **GAMES** Jen and Travis are playing a game that requires each player to roll a number cube and choose one ball from a bag without looking that contains one red, one blue, one green, and two yellow balls. The player that rolls an even number and chooses a yellow ball is the winner. What is the probability of a player rolling an even number and drawing a yellow ball without looking? $\dfrac{1}{5}$

4. **FOOD** A local bookstore offers a limited sandwich menu for their lunch-time customers. The choices are listed in the table below. How many different kinds of sandwiches does the bookstore offer?

Bread	Meat	Condiments
White	Turkey	Lettuce
Wheat	Roast Beef	Tomato
Rye	Ham	Cheese
Italian		Onions

48

LICENSE PLATES For Exercises 5–8, use the following information.
Chet noticed that most of the license plate numbers in his state have three letters, A through Z, followed by three digits, 0 through 9.

5. How many different three-letter combinations are there for a license plate? **17,576**

6. How many different three-digit combinations are there for a license plate? **1000**

7. How many different license plates can the state issue? **17,576,000**

8. The license plate on Chet's mother's car is CPD 290, which are Chet's initials. What is the probability of his mother getting that license plate? $\dfrac{1}{17,576,000}$

Answers (Lessons 12-8 and 12-9)

12-8 Enrichment

Outcomes

Complete.

1. Complete the spinner so that it will have six different possible outcomes.

2. List the numbers that could be placed on the die to provide only four different possible outcomes.
Answers will vary. Sample answer: 1, 1, 1, 2, 3, 4

The six sections do not have to be the same size.

3. Complete the spinner so that it is more likely to land on red than blue.

Red section must be larger than blue section.

4. List the months in which you could choose a date and have 30 possible outcomes.
April, June, September, November

5. There are white, green, and blue marbles in a bag. What is the minimum number of each so that it is twice as likely that you draw a green one as a white one, and three times as likely that you draw a blue one as a green one? **1 white, 2 green, and 6 blue**

6. A year between 1950 and 2001 is chosen at random. How many possible outcomes are there where the year is a leap year? List them. **13 outcomes; 1952, 1956, 1960, 1964, 1968, 1972, 1976, 1980, 1984, 1988, 1992, 1996, 2000**

12-9 Lesson Reading Guide

Permutations and Combinations

Get Ready for the Lesson

Read the introduction to Lesson 12-9 in your textbook. Write your answers below.

a. Make a list of all possible pairs for class offices. (*Note:* Lenora-Michael is different than Michael-Lenora.) **Lenora-Michael, Lenora-Nate, Lenora-Olivia, Lenora-Patrick, Michael-Lenora, Michael-Nate, Michael-Olivia, Michael-Patrick, Nate-Michael, Nate-Lenora, Nate-Olivia, Nate-Patrick, Olivia-Michael, Olivia-Lenora, Olivia-Nate, Olivia-Patrick, Patrick-Lenora, Patrick-Michael, Patrick-Nate, Patrick-Olivia**

b. How does the Fundamental Counting Principle relate to the number of pairs you found? **The results are the same.**

c. Make another list for student council seats. (*Note:* For this list, Lenora-Michael is the same as Michael-Lenora.) **Lenora-Michael, Lenora-Nate, Lenora-Olivia, Lenora-Patrick, Michael-Nate, Michael-Olivia, Michael-Patrick, Nate-Olivia, Nate-Patrick, Olivia-Patrick**

d. How does the answer in part **a** compare to the answer in part **c**? **The answer in part c equals the answer in part a divided by 2.**

Read the Lesson 1–3. See students' work.

Write a definition and give an example of each new vocabulary word.

Vocabulary	Definition	Example
1. permutation		
2. factorial		
3. combination		

Remember What You Learned

4. Complete the diagram at right by writing the words *combinations* and *permutations* in the correct blanks. Then write a sentence based on the diagram stating how to remember the difference between permutations and combinations. **Sample answer: Permutations are all of the possible outcomes, and both start with the letter *p*. Because the set of permutations contains all possible outcomes, it must be the larger set. Therefore, the smaller set of outcomes must be the set of combinations.**

Possible Outcomes or
Permutations

Combinations

Answers (Lesson 12-9)

12-9 Skills Practice

Permutations and Combinations

Tell whether each situation is a _permutation_ or _combination_. Then solve.

1. How many ways can 6 student desks be arranged in a row? **P; 720 ways**

2. How many ways can 18 baseball cards be passed out to 2 students? **C; 153 ways**

3. How many ways can 10 students line up for lunch? **P; 3,628,800 ways**

4. How many ways can you choose 4 CDs from a stack of 8 CDs? **C; 70 ways**

5. How many ways can 3 pairs of shoes be chosen from 8 pairs? **C; 56 ways**

6. How many ways can 9 runners be arranged on a 4-person relay team? **P; 3024 ways**

Find each value.

7. 9! **362,880**

8. 5! **120**

9. 3! **6**

10. 4! **24**

11. 6! **720**

12. 12! **479,001,600**

13. **SPORTS** The Eastern Division of a baseball league is composed of 5 teams. How many different ways can teams of the Eastern Division finish? **120 ways**

14. **LEISURE** The local hobby store has 17 model airplanes to display. If the front case holds 6 models, how many ways can 6 planes be chosen for the front of the store? **12,376 ways**

15. **ZOOS** The local zoo has 23 animals it can take on visits to schools and other community centers. How many ways can the zoo directors choose 9 animals for a trip to a middle school? **817,190 ways**

16. **CULTURE** There are 15 Irish dancers in a championship-level competition. How many ways can the top 3 finishers be arranged? **2730 ways**

17. **RACING** In an auto race, the cars start in 11 rows of 3. How many ways can the front row be made from the field of 33 race cars? **32,736 ways**

TELEVISION For Exercises 18 and 19, use the following information. A television network has a choice of 11 new shows for 4 consecutive time slots.

18. How many ways can four shows be chosen, without considering the age of the viewers or the popularity of the time slots? **330 ways**

19. How many ways can the shows be arranged if the time slots are during prime time and in competition for viewers? **7920 ways**

12-9 Study Guide and Intervention

Permutations and Combinations

Permutations	Words	An arrangement or listing in which order is important is called a **permutation**.
	Symbols	$P(m, n)$ means m number of choices taken n at a time.
	Example	$P(3, 2) = 3 \cdot 2 = 6$
Combinations	Words	An arrangement or listing where order is _not_ important is called a **combination**.
	Symbols	$C(m, n) = \dfrac{P(m, n)}{n!}$
	Example	$C(6, 2) = \dfrac{P(6, 2)}{2!} = \dfrac{6 \cdot 5}{2 \cdot 1}$ or 15

Example 1 SPORTS How many ways can the top five finishers be arranged in a 20-person cross-country race?

Order is important.
So, this arrangement is a permutation.

20 runners → choose 5 →

- 20 choices for 1st place
- 19 choices for 2nd place
- 18 choices for 3rd place
- 17 choices for 4th place
- 16 choices for 5th place

$P(20, 5) = 20 \cdot 19 \cdot 18 \cdot 17 \cdot 16$
= 1,860,480 ways

Example 2 SCHOOL In a science class with 42 students, how many 3-person lab teams can be formed?

Order is not important.
So, this arrangement is a combination.

From 42 students, take 3 at a time.

$C(42, 3) = \dfrac{P(42, 3)}{3!}$

$= \dfrac{42 \cdot 41 \cdot 40}{3 \cdot 2 \cdot 1}$ or 11,480 lab teams

Exercises

Tell whether each situation is a _permutation_ or _combination_. Then solve.

1. How many ways can three people be selected from a group of seven? **C; 35 ways**

2. How many ways can a 6-person kickball team be chosen from 27 students? **C; 296,010 ways**

3. How many ways can 15 actors fill 6 roles in a play? **P; 3,603,600 ways**

4. How many ways can 5 books be borrowed from a collection of 40 books? **C; 658,008 ways**

5. **JOBS** A telemarketing firm has 35 applicants for 8 identical entry-level positions. How many ways can the firm choose 8 employees? **C; 23,535,820 ways**

6. **FOOD** A pizza place sends neighbors a coupon for a 4 topping pizza of any size. If the pizzeria has 15 toppings and 3 sizes to choose from, how many possible pizzas could be purchased using the coupon? **C; 4,095 pizzas**

Answers (Lesson 12-9)

NAME _____ DATE _____ PERIOD _____

12-9 Word Problem Practice

Permutations and Combinations

1. **SOFTBALL** There are 10 players on Julia's softball team. The coach is deciding on the batting order for the next game. How many different orders does the coach have to choose the first 4 batters? **5040 ways**

2. **PIZZA** The owner of the Pizza Village wants to advertise her pizza shop on the radio. The table below shows all of the different pizzas the Pizza Village offers. How many different 1-topping pizzas can she say they offer?

Pizza Village		
Crust	**Size**	**Toppings**
Thin	Small	Extra cheese
Thick	Medium	Sausage
Deep-dish	Large	Mushrooms
		Olives
		Onions
		Vegetables
		Pepperoni
		Sausage

72

3. **FOOTBALL** Ryan and Gus play on a 6-man football team. The team has 9 players in all. How many different combination of players can their coach put on the field at any one time? **84**

4. **LICENSE PLATES** In Ohio, license plates are issued with three letters followed by four numbers. The first number cannot be zero. Numbers repeat, but letters do not. How many license plates can Ohio generate with this format? **140,400,000 license plates**

SOCIAL SECURITY NUMBERS For Exercises 5 and 6, use the following information. In the United States, each citizen is assigned a nine-digit social security number. The first three digits of the social security number are assigned based on the ZIP code in the mailing address provided on the original application form. The two middle digits of the social security number, which range from 01 through 99, are used to break all of the social security numbers within the same area number into smaller blocks. The last four digits in a social security number run consecutively from 0001 through 9999.

5. How many social security numbers that start with 467 are possible? **989,901**

6. There are 38 social security area numbers assigned to Texas. How many different social security numbers are possible? **37,616,238**

7. There are 72 areas among the 50 states and the District of Columbia. How many different social security numbers are possible? **71,272,872**

NAME _____ DATE _____ PERIOD _____

12-9 Practice

Permutations and Combinations

Tell whether each situation is a *permutation* or *combination*. Then solve.

1. How many ways can you make a sandwich by choosing 4 of 10 ingredients? **C; 210**

2. How many ways can 11 photographs be arranged horizontally? **P; 39,916,800**

3. How many ways can you buy 2 software titles from a choice of 12? **C; 66 ways**

4. How many ways can a baseball manager make a 9-player batting order from a group of 16 players? **P; 4,151,347,200 ways**

5. How many ways can 30 students be arranged in a 4-student line? **P; 657,720 ways**

6. How many ways can 3 cookie batches be chosen out of 6 prize-winning batches? **C; 20 ways**

7. **SCHOOL TRIPS** Students are chosen in groups of 6 to tour a local business. How many ways can 6 students be selected from 3 classes totaling 53 students? **22,957,480 ways**

8. **CONTESTS** In a raffle, 5 winners get to choose from 5 prizes, starting with the first name drawn. If 87 people entered the raffle, how many ways can the winners be arranged? **4,433,982,840 ways**

9. **RESTAURANTS** A local restaurant specializes in simple and tasty meals.

a. How many sandwiches are possible if the restaurant lets you build a sandwich by choosing any 4 of 10 sandwich ingredients? **210 sandwiches**

b. If there are 6 soups to choose from, how many soup-and build-a-sandwich specials are possible? **1260 specials**

10. **SPORTS** An inline skate has 4 wheels. How many ways could 4 replacement wheels be chosen from a pack of 10 wheels and fitted to a skate? **5040 ways**

GIFT WRAPPING For Exercises 11–14, use the following information.

An upscale department offers its customers free gift wrapping on any day that they spend at least $100. The store offers 5 box sizes (XS, S, M, L, XL), 6 wrapping themes (birthday, wedding, baby girl, baby boy, anniversary, and all-occasion), and 3 styles of bow (classic, modern, and jazzy).

11. How many ways can packages be gift-wrapped at the store? **90 ways**

12. What is the probability that any wrapped package will be in a large box? $\frac{1}{5}$

13. What is the probability that any wrapped package will *not* have a jazzy bow? $\frac{2}{3}$

14. What is the probability that a customer will request wrapping for a baby-boy gift? $\frac{1}{6}$

Answers (Lessons 12-9 and 12-10)

12-10 Lesson Reading Guide

Probability of Composite Events

NAME _____ DATE _____ PERIOD _____

Get Ready for the Lesson

Read the introduction to Lesson 12-10 in your textbook. Write your answers below.

a. What was your experimental probability for the red then white outcome?

See students' work; theoretical probability is $\frac{1}{4}$.

b. Would you expect the probability to be different if you did not place the first counter back in the bag? Explain your reasoning. **Yes; by not replacing the first counter drawn, you affect the possibilities for the second draw.**

Read the Lesson 1–4. See students' work.

Write a definition and give an example of each new vocabulary phrase.

Vocabulary	Definition	Example
1. composite events		
2. independent events		
3. dependent events		
4. mutually exclusive events		

You are finding the probability of choosing the following arrangements of counters from a bag containing red, orange, and blue counters. Label each situation with independent events, dependent events, or mutually exclusive events.

5. a red counter, which is replaced, followed by a blue counter   **independent events**

6. an orange counter or a primary color   **mutually exclusive events**

7. an orange counter, which is kept out of the bag, followed by a red counter   **dependent events**

Remember What You Learned

8. Complete the concept map below with the vocabulary phrases from this lesson.

Probability of Two Events

Does the outcome of the first event influence the outcome of the second event?

— yes → One event, then the other **P(A AND B)** → **dependent events**

— no → One event, or the other **P(A OR B)** → **mutually exclusive events**

→ **independent events**

Chapter 12   61   Glencoe Pre-Algebra

12-9 Enrichment

Permutations and Combinations

NAME _____ DATE _____ PERIOD _____

An arrangement of objects *in a given order* is called a **permutation** of the objects. A symbol for the number of permutations is $P(n, x)$, where x represents the number of objects to be arranged in order and n reminds us that these objects are chosen from an original set of n objects.

$$P(n, x) = \frac{n!}{(n-x)!}$$

Example 1 If gold, silver, and bronze medals are to be awarded to the first 3 finishers in an 8-person race, in how many ways can the medals be awarded?

$P(8, 3) = \frac{8!}{5!}$

$= \frac{8 \cdot 7 \cdot 6 \cdot 5 \cdot 4 \cdot 3 \cdot 2 \cdot 1}{5 \cdot 4 \cdot 3 \cdot 2 \cdot 1}$

$= 8 \cdot 7 \cdot 6$

$= 336$ ways in which the medals may be awarded

A selection of x objects taken from a set of n objects *without regard for order* of the selection is called a **combination**. A symbol for the number of combinations is $C(n, x)$.

$$C(n, x) = \frac{n!}{x!(n-x)!}$$

Example 2 In how many ways can you choose 3 people from a group of 12 without regard for order?

$C(12, 3) = \frac{12!}{3!9!}$

$= \frac{12 \cdot 11 \cdot 10 \cdot 9 \cdot 8 \cdot 7 \cdot 6 \cdot 5 \cdot 4 \cdot 3 \cdot 2 \cdot 1}{(3 \cdot 2 \cdot 1)(9 \cdot 8 \cdot 7 \cdot 6 \cdot 5 \cdot 4 \cdot 3 \cdot 2 \cdot 1)}$

$= \frac{12 \cdot 11 \cdot 10}{3 \cdot 2}$

$= 220$ possible groups of 3 people

Find each value.

1. $P(7, 2)$ **42**

2. $P(7, 5)$ **2520**

3. $C(7, 2)$ **21**

4. $C(7, 5)$ **21**

5. $P(13, 2)$ **156**

6. $C(13, 11)$ **78**

Chapter 12   60   Glencoe Pre-Algebra

Answers (Lesson 12-10)

NAME _____ DATE _____ PERIOD _____

12-10 Skills Practice

Probability of Composite Events

A number cube is rolled and the spinner is spun. Find each probability.

1. $P(2$ and green triangle) $\dfrac{1}{48}$

2. $P($an odd number and a circle) $\dfrac{1}{8}$

3. $P($a prime number and a quadrilateral) $\dfrac{1}{4}$

4. $P($a number greater than 4 and a parallelogram) $\dfrac{1}{8}$

There are 5 yellow marbles, 1 purple marble, 3 green marbles, and 3 red marbles in a bag. Once a marble is drawn, it is replaced. Find the probability of each outcome.

5. a purple then a red marble $\dfrac{1}{48}$

6. a red then a green marble $\dfrac{1}{16}$

7. two green marbles in a row $\dfrac{1}{16}$

8. two red marbles in a row $\dfrac{1}{16}$

9. a purple then a green marble $\dfrac{1}{48}$

10. a red then a yellow marble $\dfrac{5}{48}$

There are 4 yellow marbles, 3 purple marbles, 1 green marble, and 1 white marble in a bag. Once a marble is drawn, it is *not* replaced. Find the probability of each outcome.

11. a purple then a white marble $\dfrac{1}{24}$

12. a white then a green marble $\dfrac{1}{72}$

13. two purple marbles in a row $\dfrac{1}{12}$

14. two yellow marbles in a row $\dfrac{1}{6}$

15. a yellow then a purple marble $\dfrac{1}{6}$

16. a green then a white marble $\dfrac{1}{72}$

A card is drawn from a standard deck of cards. Find the probability of each outcome.

17. $P($a red card or a club) $\dfrac{3}{4}$

18. $P($a diamond or a spade) $\dfrac{1}{2}$

19. $P($a face card or a 2) $\dfrac{4}{13}$

20. $P($a 7 or a 9) $\dfrac{2}{13}$

21. $P($a red card or a king of spades) $\dfrac{27}{52}$

22. $P($a heart or a queen of diamonds) $\dfrac{7}{26}$

NAME _____ DATE _____ PERIOD _____

12-10 Study Guide and Intervention

Probability of Composite Events

Probability of Two Independent Events	Words	The probability of two independent events is found by multiplying the probability of the first event by the probability of the second event.
	Symbols	$P(A$ and $B) = P(A) \cdot P(B)$
Probability of Two Dependent Events	Words	If two events, A and B, are dependent, then the probability of events occurring is the product of the probability of A and the probability of B after A occurs.
	Symbols	$P(A$ and $B) = P(A) \cdot P(B$ following $A)$

Example 1 **GAMES** A card is drawn from a standard deck of 52 cards. The card is replaced and another is drawn. Find the probability if the first card is the 3 of hearts and the second card is the 2 of clubs.

Since the first card is replaced, the events are independent.

$P(3$ of hearts and 2 of clubs$) = P(3$ of hearts$) \cdot P(2$ of clubs$)$

$= \dfrac{1}{52} \cdot \dfrac{1}{52}$

$= \dfrac{1}{2704}$

The probability is $\dfrac{1}{2704}$.

Probability of Mutually Exclusive Events	Words	The probability of one or the other of two **mutually exclusive events** can be found by adding the probability of the first event to the probability of the second event.
	Symbols	$P(A$ or $B) = P(A) + P(B)$

Example 2 The spinner at the right is spun. What is the probability that the spinner will stop on 7 or an even number?

The events are mutually exclusive because the spinner cannot stop on both 7 and an even number at the same time.

$P(7$ or even$) = P(7) + P($even$) = \dfrac{1}{8} + \dfrac{4}{8} = \dfrac{5}{8}$

The probability that the spinner will stop on 7 or an even number is $\dfrac{5}{8}$.

Exercises

A card is drawn from a standard deck of cards. The card is not replaced and a second card is drawn. Find each probability.

1. $P(4$ and 8$)$ $\dfrac{4}{663}$

2. $P($queen of hearts and 10$)$ $\dfrac{1}{663}$

A card is drawn from a standard deck of cards. Find each probability.

3. $P($queen of clubs or a red card$)$ $\dfrac{27}{52}$

4. $P($queen of hearts or 10$)$ $\dfrac{5}{52}$

Answers (Lesson 12-10)

(Lesson 12-10)

Lesson 12-10

NAME _____ DATE _____ PERIOD _____

12-10 Word Problem Practice

Probability of Composite Events

1. BIRTHDAYS Sarah's birthday and Dakota's birthday are both in May. What is the probability that their birthdays are the same day in May?

$\dfrac{1}{961}$

2. GAMES Marvin and Greg are playing a card game. The deck of cards has 25 red cards, 25 yellow cards, 25 blue cards, 25 green cards, and 8 wild cards. Marvin shuffles the deck two times before he starts to deal the cards. What is the probability that the first card Marvin deals is yellow or wild card?

$\dfrac{33}{108}$

3. DOMINOES A set of dominoes contains 91 tiles, with the numbers on the tiles ranging from 0 to 12. There are 13 tiles that have the same number on each end. These tiles are called doubles. To begin a game, each player draws one tile, which is not returned to the pile. What is the probability that the first and second players each draw a double?

$\dfrac{2}{105}$

4. MONEY Mr. Santiago pulls two bills at random from the 4 $1 bills, 3 $5 bills, and 1 $20 bill in his pocket. What is the probability that he chooses one $1 bill and one $5 bill?

$\dfrac{3}{14}$

ANALYZE GRAPHS For Exerercises 5 and 6, use the information below.

The graph shows the favorite sports team of teens between the ages of 15 and 18.

Favorite Sports Team

Source: www.sianats.com/sianatsdaily/sianatsdata/v2Dno11.htm

5. What is the probability that one teen likes the Dallas Cowboys and another likes the Atlanta Braves? Express as a percent rounded to the nearest tenth.

0.5%

6. What is the probability that one teen likes the L.A. Lakers and another likes the N.Y. Yankees? Express as a percent rounded to the nearest thousandth.

0.012

Chapter 12

Glencoe Pre-Algebra

Copyright © Glencoe/McGraw-Hill, a division of The McGraw-Hill Companies, Inc.

NAME _____ DATE _____ PERIOD _____

12-10 Practice

Probability of Composite Events

An eight-sided die is rolled and the spinner is spun. Find each probability.

1. P(4 and yellow fruit or vegetable) $\dfrac{1}{32}$

2. P(an odd number and a pumpkin) $\dfrac{1}{16}$

3. P(a prime number and a red fruit or vegetable) $\dfrac{1}{8}$

4. P(a number less than 4 and a blue fruit or vegetable) $\dfrac{3}{64}$

There are 6 orange marbles, 2 red marbles, 3 white marbles, and 4 green marbles in a bag. Once a marble is drawn, it is replaced. Find the probability of each outcome.

5. a red then a white marble $\dfrac{2}{75}$

6. a white then a green marble $\dfrac{4}{75}$

7. two orange marbles in a row $\dfrac{4}{25}$

8. two marbles in a row that are *not* white $\dfrac{16}{25}$

9. a green then a *not* green marble $\dfrac{44}{225}$

10. a red then an orange then a green marble $\dfrac{16}{1125}$

There are 2 green marbles, 7 blue marbles, 3 white marbles, and 4 purple marbles in a bag. Once a marble is drawn, it is *not* replaced. Find the probability of each outcome.

11. a green then a white marble $\dfrac{1}{40}$

12. a blue then a purple marble $\dfrac{7}{60}$

13. two blue marbles in a row $\dfrac{7}{40}$

14. two marbles in a row that are *not* purple $\dfrac{11}{20}$

15. a white then a purple marble $\dfrac{1}{20}$

16. three purple marbles in a row $\dfrac{1}{140}$

The chart shows the letter-number combinations for bingo. The balls are randomly drawn one at a time. Balls are *not* replaced after they are drawn. Find the probability of each outcome.

B	I	N	G	O
1	13	25	37	49
2	14	26	38	50
3	15	27	39	51
4	16	28	40	52
5	17	29	41	53
6	18	30	42	54
7	19	31	43	55
8	20	32	44	56
9	21	33	45	57
10	22	34	46	58
11	23	35	47	59
12	24	36	48	60

17. a B-1 $\dfrac{1}{60}$

18. a G $\dfrac{1}{5}$

19. an N or a B-2 $\dfrac{13}{60}$

20. an I or an O $\dfrac{2}{5}$

21. *not* a G $\dfrac{4}{5}$

22. a B-6, then a G, then another G $\dfrac{11}{17,110}$

Chapter 12

64

Glencoe Pre-Algebra

Copyright © Glencoe/McGraw-Hill, a division of The McGraw-Hill Companies, Inc.

Chapter 12

A31

Glencoe Pre-Algebra

Answers (Lesson 12-10)

NAME _____ DATE _____ PERIOD _____

Probability of Dependent Events

Look at the letters in the word MATHEMATICAL. If these letters were placed in a hat, what would be the probability of drawing a vowel and then, without replacing the vowel, drawing a consonant? These are **dependent events** since the letter selected on the first draw affects the probability for the second draw.

$$P(\text{vowel, then consonant}) = \frac{5}{12} \cdot \frac{7}{11} = \frac{35}{132}$$

Find the probability of drawing each of the following from the letters in MATHEMATICAL if the letters are not replaced.

1. two Ms $\dfrac{1}{66}$

2. two As $\dfrac{1}{22}$

3. three As $\dfrac{1}{220}$

4. three vowels $\dfrac{1}{22}$

5. five consonants $\dfrac{7}{264}$

6. the letters MATH in that order $\dfrac{1}{990}$

Now, think of using variables instead of numbers. This is very useful, since this is the way formulas are developed. Once a formula is found, it can be used for any numbers. Begin by examining the following example.

Example Three of 10 socks in a box are blue. If socks are drawn without looking and not replaced, what is the probability of picking 3 blue socks in 3 drawings?

$$\frac{3}{10} \cdot \frac{2}{9} \cdot \frac{1}{8} = \frac{6}{720}, \text{ or } \frac{1}{120}$$

7. If box containing n socks has k blue ones, what is the probability of picking 3 blue socks in 3 drawings?

$$\frac{k}{n} \cdot \frac{k-1}{n-1} \cdot \frac{k-2}{n-2}$$

8. If a box containing n socks has k blue ones, what is the probability of picking x blue socks in x drawings?

$$\frac{k}{n} \cdot \frac{k-1}{n-1} \cdot \frac{k-2}{n-2} \cdot \ldots \cdot \frac{k-(x-1)}{n-(x-1)}$$

9. Use your formula from Exercise 7 to find the probability of picking 3 blue socks in 3 drawings from a box containing 6 socks, 4 of them blue.

$$\frac{4}{6} \cdot \frac{3}{5} \cdot \frac{2}{4} = \frac{1}{5}$$

10. Use your formula from Exercise 8 to find the probability of picking 4 blue socks in 4 drawings from a box containing 6 socks, 5 of them blue.

$$\frac{5}{6} \cdot \frac{4}{5} \cdot \frac{3}{4} \cdot \frac{2}{3} = \frac{1}{3}$$

Chapter 12   66   Glencoe Pre-Algebra

Copyright © Glencoe/McGraw-Hill, a division of The McGraw-Hill Companies, Inc.

12-10 Spreadsheet Activity

NAME _____ DATE _____ PERIOD _____

Simulating a Composite Probability

Acting out a probability situation is called a **simulation**. You can use a spreadsheet to simulate compound events and investigate compound probability.

Example A typical mare can give birth once a year. **What is the probability that Rebeca's mare will bear female foals in two consecutive years?**

Step 1 Use the random number generator of the spreadsheet to simulate the events. The formula RANDBETWEEN(0,1) will give a random number between 0 and 1. Let 0 represent a male foal and 1 represent a female foal.

Column A represents the first foal and Column B represents the second. Since 1 represents a female and 0 represents a male, Column C is the sum of Columns A and B, the number of female foals.

	A	B	C
	First Foal	Second Foal	Number of Females
1			
2	0	1	1
3	1	0	1
4	1	1	2
5	1	0	1
6	0	0	0
7	0	1	1
8	1	1	2
9	1	0	1
10	0	0	0
11	0	1	1

Step 2 Use the spreadsheet to conduct 10 trials. Record the number of times that there are 2 females.

Exercises

1. Use the formula $P(A \text{ and } B) = P(A) \cdot P(B)$ to find the probability that Rebeca's mare will bear female foals in two consecutive years. $\dfrac{1}{4}$

2. Based on your simulation, in what fraction of the 10 trials are there 2 females? How does this compare to the probability that you found in Exercise 1? **See students' work.**

3. Expand your simulation to 100 trials by clicking on the cells in the bottom row and dragging downward. In what fraction of the 100 trials are there 2 females? How does this compare to the fractions that you found in Exercises 1 and 2? **See students' work.**

4. What is the probability that Rebeca's mare will bear female foals in three consecutive years? Use the spreadsheet to simulate three foals. In what fraction of the trials are there 3 females? How does this compare to the probability? $\dfrac{1}{8}$; **See students' work.**

Chapter 12   67   Glencoe Pre-Algebra

Copyright © Glencoe/McGraw-Hill, a division of The McGraw-Hill Companies, Inc.

Chapter 12   A32   Glencoe Pre-Algebra

Chapter 12 Assessment Answer Key

Quiz 1 (Lessons 12-1 through 12-3) Page 71

1.

Stem	Leaf
4	5 7 9 9 9
5	2 7
6	4
7	3 $4|5 = 45$

2. _____40–49_____

3. _____62_____

4. _____70.5; 48.5_____

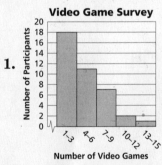

5. _____22_____

Quiz 2 (Lessons 12-4 and 12-5) Page 71

1.

Video Game Survey

(bar graph: Number of Participants vs. Number of Video Games)
1-3: 18, 4-6: 11, 7-9: 7, 10-12: 2, 13-15: 1

2. _____39_____

3. _____10_____

4. _____circle graph_____

5. _____venn diagram_____

Quiz 3 (Lessons 12-6 and 12-7) Page 72

1. Sample answer: wider column could give the impression that a larger number is being represented by that column.

2. **Each symbol represents a different number of people**

3. **the 2nd one; it looks like it is 8:4 who prefer cats**

4. $\dfrac{1}{6}$

5. $\dfrac{1}{2}$

Quiz 4 (Lessons 12-8 and 12-10) Page 72

1. _____32_____

2. _____12_____

3. _____$\dfrac{1}{36}$_____

4. _permutation; 120_

5. $\dfrac{2}{7}$

Mid-Chapter Test Page 73

1. ___B___

2. ___H___

3. ___A___

4. ___G___

5.

Test Scores

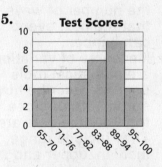

(bar graph: Test Scores)
65-70: 4, 71-76: 3, 77-82: 5, 83-88: 7, 89-94: 9, 95-100: 4

6. _____25_____

7. _____line graph_____

8. _____bar graph_____

Chapter 12 Assessment Answer Key

Vocabulary Test
Page 74

1. stem-and leaf plot
2. stems
3. interquartile range
4. box-and-whisker plot
5. outliers
6. histogram
7. permutation
8. range
9. independent
10. mutually exclusive events
11. The Fundamental Counting Principle tells you how many possible outcomes you can get from a certain number of choices. It says that to find the number of possible outcomes, multiply the number of ways that one event can happen by the number of ways that the next event can happen.
12. Measures of variation are statistical tools used to describe how spread out or close together the data are. They include range, median, upper and lower quartiles, and interquartile range.
13. The data for two stem-and-leaf plots are plotted together, with the center column containing the stem for both plots. The leaves then spread out to the left for one set of data, and to the right for the other set of data. This way the two sets of data can be compared easily and fairly.

Form 1
Page 75

1. __D__
2. __G__
3. __B__
4. __J__
5. __D__
6. __H__
7. __B__
8. __H__
9. __C__
10. __H__
11. __D__

Page 76

12. __G__
13. __C__
14. __F__
15. __C__
16. __J__
17. __A__
18. __H__
19. __C__
20. __F__

B: __$\frac{2}{145}$__

Chapter 12 Assessment Answer Key

Form 2A
Page 77

Page 78

Form 2B
Page 79

Page 80

10. H

1. A

11. B

12. G

2. H

13. B

3. B

14. J

4. F

15. A

5. B

16. G

6. J

17. A

7. A

18. F

19. B

8. H

20. F

9. A

B: 15

1. C

2. F

3. C

4. G

5. B

6. H

7. B

8. J

9. C

10. G

11. D

12. J

13. A

14. G

15. C

16. J

17. C

18. G

19. D

20. H

Sample answer: 10, 15, 18, 19, 24, 26, 32, 35, 37, 40

B:

Answers

Chapter 12 Assessment Answer Key

Form 2C
Page 81

Olympic Medals

1.

Stem	Leaf
2	5 8 9
3	4 8
4	
5	7 9
6	8
7	
8	8
9	7

$3\,|\,4 = 34$

2. _____ 7 _____

3. _____ 72; 39 _____

4. **Sample answer: They are close together.**

5.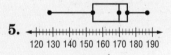

6. _____ 21 _____

7. _____ 25% _____

8.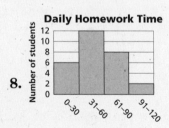

9. _____ 10 _____

10.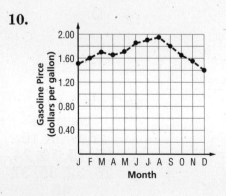

Page 82

11. _____ 72 _____

12. _____ $\dfrac{1}{1,000,000}$ _____

13. **combination; 210**

14. **permutation; 504**

15. _____ 132 _____

16. _____ 720 _____

17. _____ $\dfrac{1}{32}$ _____

18. _____ $\dfrac{1}{28}$ _____

19. _____ $\dfrac{2}{3}$ _____

20. _____ $\dfrac{5}{6}$ _____

B: _____ $\dfrac{1}{52,360}$ _____

Chapter 12 Assessment Answer Key

Form 2D
Page 83

Page 84

1.
Olympic Medals

Stem	Leaf
0	8
1	0 2 3 3 4 7 8
2	6 8

$2|6 = 26$

2. _____ 4 _____

3. _____ 20; 6 _____

4. Sample answer: They are far apart.

5.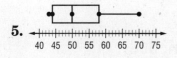

6. _____ 14 _____

7. _____ 50% _____

8.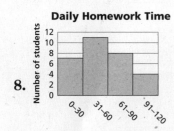
Daily Homework Time

9. _____ 12 _____

10. Sample answer: Yes, the graph is misleading because the vertical scale does not start at zero.

11. _____ 144 _____

12. _____ $\dfrac{1}{100,000}$ _____

13. _____ combination; 252 _____

14. _____ permutation; 1680 _____

15. _____ 24 _____

16. _____ 720 _____

17. _____ $\dfrac{1}{64}$ _____

18. _____ $\dfrac{1}{5}$ _____

19. _____ $\dfrac{5}{6}$ _____

20. _____ $\dfrac{1}{6}$ _____

B: _____ 35 _____

Answers

Chapter 12 Assessment Answer Key

Form 3
Page 85

Page 86

1. _____ 116 _____

2. _____ 16 _____

3. _____ 84 _____

4. **The interquartile range of the American League is greater than the interquartile range of the National League.**

5.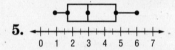

6. _____ 75% _____

7. _____ 30 _____

8. _____ 40 _____

9. _____ 55% _____

10. **Sample answer: Yes, because the horizontal scale is divided into unequal increments. This gives the appearance that twice as many 18–24 year olds see at least one movie per month as 25–34 year olds.**

11. _____ 12 _____

12. _____ 1024 _____

13. _____ $\dfrac{1}{10,000}$ _____

14. combination; 210

15. permutation; 336

16. combination; 120

17. _____ $\dfrac{1}{5}, \dfrac{14}{15}$ _____

18. _____ $\dfrac{1}{64}$ _____

19. _____ $\dfrac{1}{12}$ _____

20. _____ $\dfrac{1}{4}$ _____

B: _____ $\dfrac{4}{13}$ _____

Chapter 12 Assessment Answer Key

Page 87, Extended-Response Test
Scoring Rubric

Score	General Description	Specific Criteria
4	**Superior** A correct solution that is supported by well-developed, accurate explanations	• Shows thorough understanding of the concepts of *variation, range, quartiles, interquartile range, stem-and-leaf plots, box-and-whisker plots, combinations, probability, simulations,* and *independent, dependent, and mutually exclusive events.* • Uses appropriate strategies to solve problems. • Computations are correct. • Written explanations are exemplary. • Graphs are accurate and appropriate. • Goes beyond requirements of some or all problems.
3	**Satisfactory** A generally correct solution, but may contain minor flaws in reasoning or computation	• Shows an understanding of the concepts of *variation, range, quartiles, interquartile range, stem-and-leaf plots, box-and-whisker plots, combinations, probability, simulations,* and *independent, dependent, and mutually exclusive events.* • Uses appropriate strategies to solve problems. • Computations are mostly correct. • Written explanations are effective. • Graphs are mostly accurate and appropriate. • Satisfies all requirements of problems.
2	**Nearly Satisfactory** A partially correct interpretation and/or solution to the problem	• Shows an understanding of the concepts of *variation, range, quartiles, interquartile range, stem-and-leaf plots, box-and-whisker plots, combinations, probability, simulations,* and *independent, dependent, and mutually exclusive events.* • May not use appropriate strategies to solve problems. • Computations are mostly correct. • Written explanations are satisfactory. • Graphs are mostly accurate. • Satisfies the requirements of most of the problems.
1	**Nearly Unsatisfactory** A correct solution with no supporting evidence or explanation	• Final computation is mostly or partially correct. • No written explanations or work is shown to substantiate the final computation. • Graphs may be accurate but lack detail or explanation. • Satisfies minimal requirements of some of the problems.
0	**Unsatisfactory** An incorrect solution indicating no mathematical understanding of the concept or task, or no solution is given	• Shows little or no understanding of the concepts of *variation, range, quartiles, interquartile range, stem-and-leaf plots, box-and-whisker plots, combinations, probability, simulations,* and *independent, dependent, and mutually exclusive events.* • Does not use appropriate strategies to solve problems. • Computations are incorrect. • Written explanations are unsatisfactory. • Graphs are inaccurate or inappropriate. • Does not satisfy the requirements of problems. • No answer may be given.

Chapter 12 Assessment Answer Key

Page 87, Extended-Response Test
Sample Answers

In addition to the scoring rubric found on page A39, the following sample answers may be used as guidance in evaluating open-ended assessment items.

1a. Range: The difference between the least and the greatest number in a set of data. Interquartile Range: The range of the middle half of the data.

1b. 5, 6, 10, 12, 16, 17, 18, 19

1c. 10, 15, 18, 19, 24, 26, 32, 35, 37, 40

1d. See students' plots. The whisker plot shows that the highest score is 40, the lowest score is 10, the median is 25, the lower quartile is 18, and the upper quartile is 35.

2. See students' graphs and explanations.

3. Sample answer: If I were a salesperson selling shorts in white or brown in sizes small, medium, and large, I would be sure to have all six options on hand to demonstrate.

4a. Use the spinners shown below and conduct an experiment.

Juan   Tony

4b. The probability of two independent events can be found by multiplying the probability of the first event by the probability of the second event. The probability of both getting a hit is 0.2×0.25 or 0.05.

4c. If Juan and Tony getting hits are mutually exclusive events, the probability is $0.20 + 0.25$ or 0.45. The events are not mutually exclusive because the two events could happen at the same time.

Chapter 12 Assessment Answer Key

Standardized Test Practice

Page 88

Page 89

1. Ⓐ Ⓑ ● Ⓓ

2. Ⓕ Ⓖ ● Ⓙ

3. Ⓐ Ⓑ Ⓒ ●

4. ● Ⓖ Ⓗ Ⓙ

5. Ⓐ Ⓑ ● Ⓓ

6. Ⓕ Ⓖ Ⓗ ●

7. Ⓐ ● Ⓒ Ⓓ

8. Ⓕ ● Ⓗ Ⓙ

9. Ⓐ Ⓑ Ⓒ ●

10. Ⓕ Ⓖ ● Ⓙ

11. Ⓐ Ⓑ ● Ⓓ

12. Ⓕ Ⓖ Ⓗ ●

13. Ⓐ Ⓑ ● Ⓓ

14. ● Ⓖ Ⓗ Ⓙ

15. Ⓐ Ⓑ Ⓒ ●

16. Ⓕ Ⓖ ● Ⓙ

17. 2 1 6 .

18. 5 0 4 0 .

Answers

Chapter 12 Assessment Answer Key

Standardized Test Practice

Page 90

19.

Stem	Leaf
0	9
1	0 3 8 8
2	1 1 2 6
3	4

1 | 0 = 10 home runs

20. $\dfrac{9}{20}$; this represents the number of kilograms in 1 pound.

21. 11.1%

22. 3; −7

23. −5

24. 11.25 feet

25. $A'(6, -1)$, $B'(1, -2)$, $C'(3, -6)$, $D'(5, -5)$

26. Sample answer $\overleftrightarrow{AD}$ and $\overleftrightarrow{GH}$

27. 120

28. 210

29a. $\dfrac{1}{36}$

29b. $\dfrac{1}{18}$; $\dfrac{1}{12}$; $\dfrac{1}{9}$, $\dfrac{5}{36}$; $\dfrac{1}{6}$; $\dfrac{5}{36}$; $\dfrac{1}{9}$; $\dfrac{1}{12}$; $\dfrac{1}{18}$; $\dfrac{1}{36}$

29c. 1